Student Edition

Eureka Math
Grade 2
Modules 7 & 8

Special thanks go to the Gordon A. Cain Center and to the Department of Mathematics at Louisiana State University for their support in the development of *Eureka Math*.

For a free *Eureka Math* Teacher
Resource Pack, Parent Tip
Sheets, and more please
visit www.Eureka.tools

Published by the non-profit Great Minds™

Copyright © 2015 Great Minds. No part of this work may be reproduced, sold, or commercialized, in whole or in part, without written permission from Great Minds. Non-commercial use is licensed pursuant to a Creative Commons Attribution-NonCommercial-ShareAlike 4.0 license; for more information, go to http://greatminds.net/maps/math/copyright. "Great Minds" and "Eureka Math" are registered trademarks of Great Minds.

Printed in the U.S.A.
This book may be purchased from the publisher at eureka-math.org
10 9 8 7 6 5 4 3

ISBN 978-1-63255-296-9

Name _____   Date _____

1. Count and categorize each picture to complete the table with tally marks.

No Legs	2 Legs	4 Legs

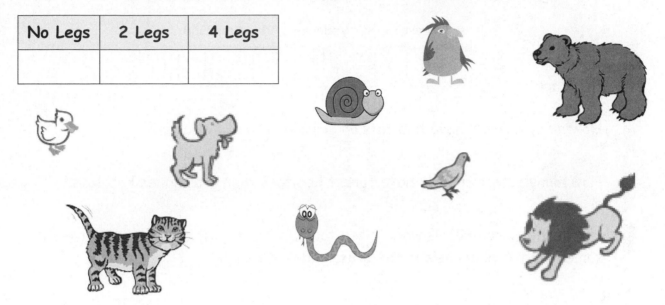

2. Count and categorize each picture to complete the table with numbers.

Fur	Feathers

EUREKA
MATH™

Lesson 1:   Sort and record data into a table using up to four categories; use category counts to solve word problems.

1

3. Use the table to answer the following questions.

Number of Animals that Live in Different Habitats		
Forest	Wetlands	Grasslands
卌 I	卌	卌 卌 IIII

a. How many animals have habitats on grasslands and wetlands? _____

b. How many fewer animals have forest habitats than grasslands habitats? _____

c. How many more animals would need to be in the forest category to have the same number as animals in the grasslands category? _____

d. How many total animal habitats were used to create this table? _____

Lesson 1:   Sort and record data into a table using up to four categories; use category counts to solve word problems.

4. Use the Animal Classification table to answer the following questions about the types of animals Ms. Lee's second-grade class found in the local zoo.

Animal Classification			
Birds	Fish	Mammals	Reptiles
6	5	11	3

a. How many animals are birds, fish, or reptiles? _____

b. How many more birds and mammals are there than fish and reptiles? _____

c. How many animals were classified? _____

d. How many more animals would need to be added to the chart to have 35 animals classified? _____

e. If 5 more birds and 2 more reptiles were added to the table, how many fewer reptiles would there be than birds? _____

Lesson 1: Sort and record data into a table using up to four categories; use category counts to solve word problems.

3

This page intentionally left blank

Name _____   Date _____

1. Count and categorize each picture to complete the table with tally marks.

No Legs	2 Legs	4 Legs

2. Count and categorize each picture to complete the table with numbers.

Fur	Feathers

EUREKA MATH

Lesson 1: Sort and record data into a table using up to four categories; use category counts to solve word problems.

5

©2015 Great Minds. eureka-math.org
G2-M7M8-SE-B4-1.3.1-01.2016

3. Use the table to answer the following questions.

Number of Animals that Live in Different Habitats		
Arctic	Forest	Grasslands
6	11	9

a. How many animals live in the arctic? ____

b. How many animals have habitats in the forest and grasslands? ____

c. How many fewer animals have arctic habitats than forest habitats? ____

d. How many more animals would need to be in the grasslands category to have the same number as the arctic and forest categories combined? ____

e. How many total animal habitats were used to create this table? ____

Lesson 1:   Sort and record data into a table using up to four categories; use category counts to solve word problems.

4. Use the Animal Classification table to answer the following questions about the class pets in West Chester Elementary School.

Animal Classification			
Birds	Fish	Mammals	Reptiles
7	15	18	9

a. How many animals are birds, fish, or reptiles? ____

b. How many more birds and mammals are there than fish and reptiles? ____

c. How many animals were classified? ____

d. If 3 more birds and 4 more reptiles were added to the table, how many fewer birds would there be than reptiles? ____

EUREKA MATH

Lesson 1: Sort and record data into a table using up to four categories; use category counts to solve word problems.

7

This page intentionally left blank

Name _____   Date _____

1. Use grid paper to create a picture graph below using data provided in the table. Then, answer the questions.

Central Park Zoo Animal Classification			
Birds	Fish	Mammals	Reptiles
6	5	11	3

Title: _____

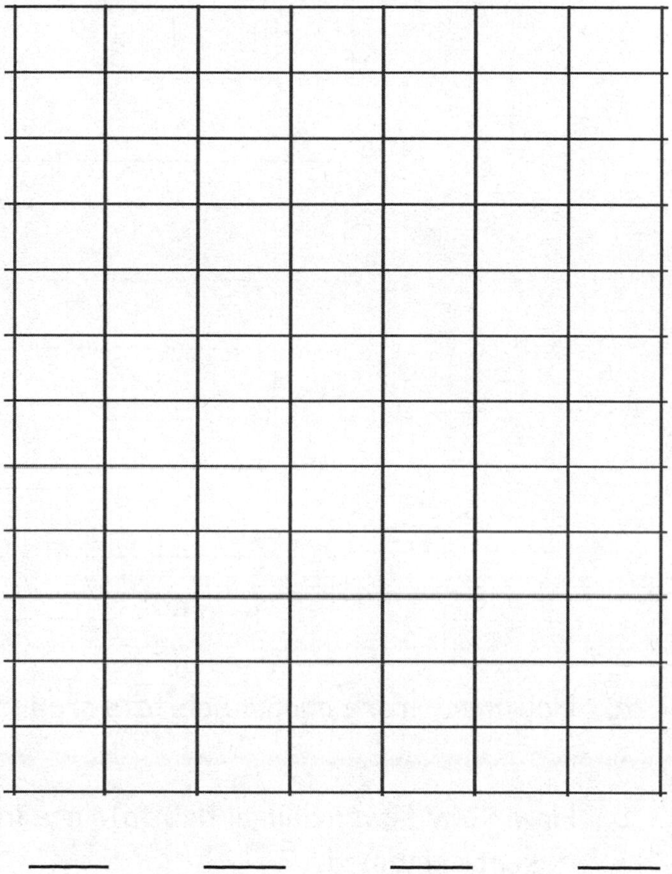

a. How many more animals are mammals than fish? _____

b. How many more animals are mammals and fish than birds and reptiles? _____

c. How many fewer animals are reptiles than mammals? _____

___ ___ ___ ___

Legend: _____

d. Write and answer your own comparison question based on the data.

Question: _____

Answer: _____

EUREKA MATH

Lesson 2:   Draw and label a picture graph to represent data with up to four categories.

9

2. Use the table below to create a picture graph in the space provided.

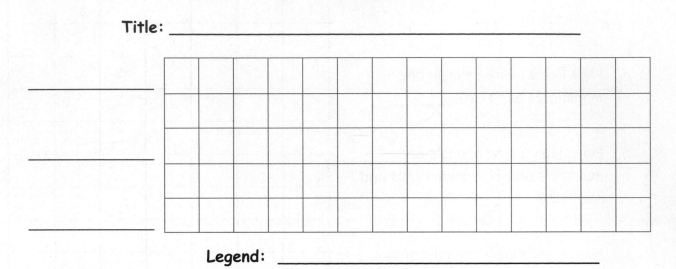

Number of Animals that Live in Different Habitats		
Desert	Tundra	Grasslands
‖‖‖ I	‖‖‖	‖‖‖ ‖‖‖ ‖‖‖ |‖‖

Title: _____

Legend: _____

a. How many more animal habitats are in the grasslands than in the desert? _____

b. How many fewer animal habitats are in the tundra than in the grasslands and desert combined? _____

c. Write and answer your own comparison question based on the data.

Question: _____

Answer: _____

Lesson 2: Draw and label a picture graph to represent data with up to four categories.

Name _____   Date _____

1. Use grid paper to create a picture graph below using data provided in the table.
    Then, answer the questions.

Favorite Mammals			
Tiger	Panda	Snow Leopard	Gorilla
8	11	7	12

Title: _____

a. How many more people chose
    gorilla as their favorite mammal
    than chose tiger? _____

b. How many more people chose
    tiger and gorilla as their favorite
    mammals than panda and snow
    leopard? _____

c. How many fewer people chose
    tiger as their favorite mammal
    than panda? _____

___   ___   ___   ___

Legend: _____

d. Write and answer your own comparison question based on the data.

Question: _____

Answer: _____

EUREKA MATH   Lesson 2:   Draw and label a picture graph to represent data with up to four   11
                                categories.

©2015 Great Minds. eureka-math.org
G2-M7M8-SE-B4-1.3.1-01.2016

2. Use the data of Mr. Clark's class vote to create a picture graph in the space provided.

Favorite Birds		
Penguin	Flamingo	Peacock
卌 l	卌	卌 卌 llll

Title: _____

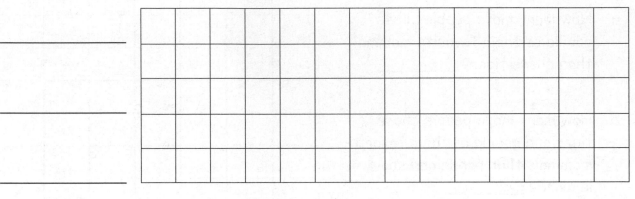

_____

_____

_____

Legend: _____

a. How many more students voted for peacocks than penguins? _____

b. How many fewer votes are for flamingos than penguins and peacocks? _____

c. Write and answer your own comparison question based on the data.

Question: _____

Answer: _____

Lesson 2:   Draw and label a picture graph to represent data with up to four categories.

Legend: _____

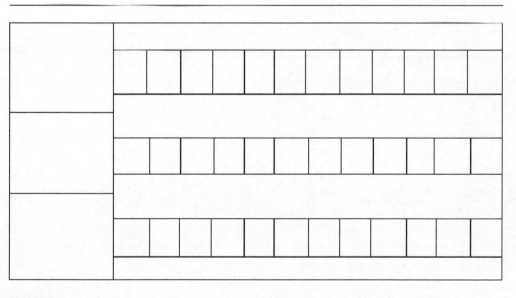

Legend: _____

vertical and horizontal picture graphs

Lesson 2:   Draw and label a picture graph to represent data with up to four
categories.

©2015 Great Minds. eureka-math.org
G2-M7M8-SE-B4-1.3.1-01.2016

This page intentionally left blank

_____

Legend: _____

_____

vertical picture graph

Lesson 2:   Draw and label a picture graph to represent data with up to four
categories.

15

This page intentionally left blank

Name _____   Date _____

1. Complete the bar graph below using data provided in the table. Then, answer the questions about the data.

Animal Classification			
Birds	Fish	Mammals	Reptiles
6	5	11	3

Title: _____

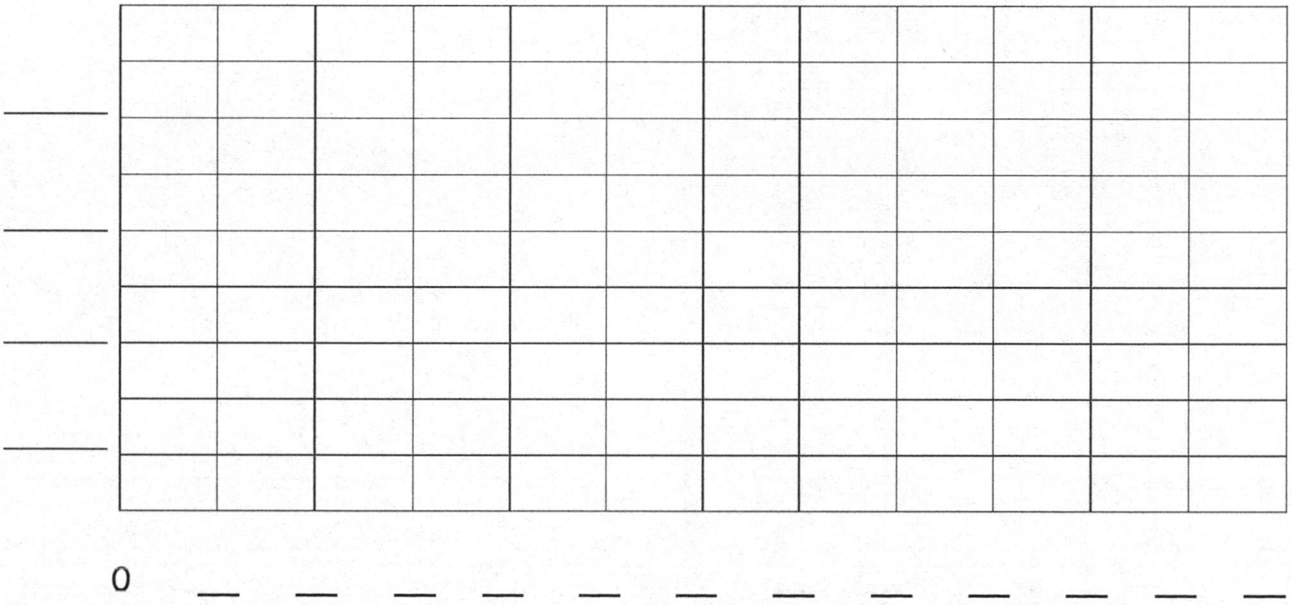

0

a. How many more animals are birds than reptiles? _____

b. How many more birds and mammals are there than fish and reptiles? _____

c. How many fewer animals are reptiles and fish than mammals? _____

d. Write and answer your own comparison question based on the data.

Question: _____

Answer: _____

2. Complete the bar graph below using data provided in the table.

Number of Animals that Live in Different Habitats		
Desert	Arctic	Grasslands
卌 I	卌	卌 卌 IIII

Title: _____

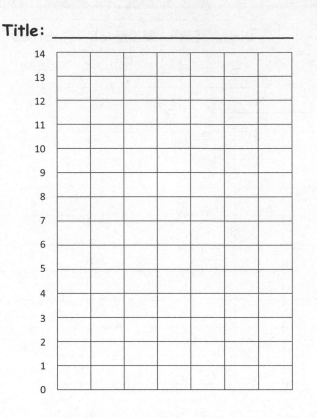

a. How many more animals live in the grasslands and arctic habitats combined than in the desert? _____

b. If 3 more grasslands animals and 4 more arctic animals are added to the graph, how many grasslands and arctic animals would there be? _____

c. If 3 animals were removed from each category, how many animals would there be? _____

d. Write your own comparison question based on the data, and answer it.

Question: _____

Answer: _____

Lesson 3:   Draw and label a bar graph to represent data; relate the count scale to the number line.

Name _____   Date _____

1. Complete the bar graph below using data provided in the table. Then, answer the questions about the data.

Number of Animals with Different Coverings at Jake's Pet Shop			
Fur	Feathers	Shells	Scales
12	9	8	11

Title: _____

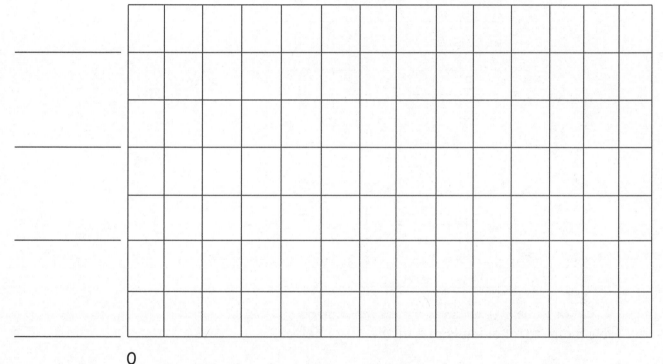

0 _ _ _ _ _ _ _ _ _ _ _ _ _ _

a. How many more animals have fur than shells? _____

b. Which pair of categories has more, fur and feathers or shells and scales? (Circle one.) How much more? _____

c. Write and answer your own comparison question based on the data.

Question: _____

Answer: _____

Lesson 3:   Draw and label a bar graph to represent data; relate the count scale to the number line.

19

©2015 Great Minds. eureka-math.org
G2-M7M8-SE-B4-1.3.1-01.2016

2. Complete the bar graph below using data provided in the table.

Number of Animals with Different Diets at the City Shelter		
Meat Only	Plants Only	Meat and Plants
卌 |||	卌 ||||	卌 卌 ||||

Title: _____

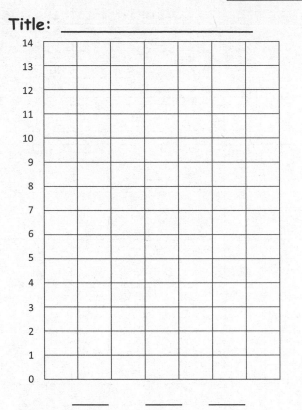

a. How many total animals are in the city shelter? _____

b. How many more meat- and plant-eating animals are there than meat only? _____

c. If 3 animals were removed from each category, how many animals would there be? _____

d. Write your own comparison question based on the data, and answer it.

Question: _____

Answer: _____

Lesson 3:   Draw and label a bar graph to represent data; relate the count scale to the number line.

EUREKA MATH™

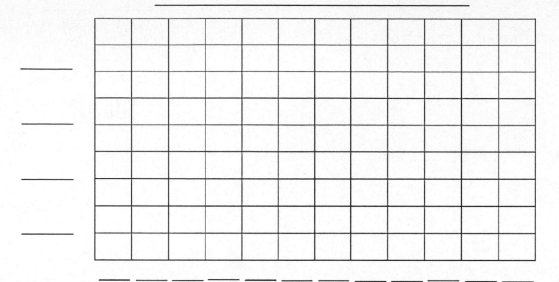

Title: _____

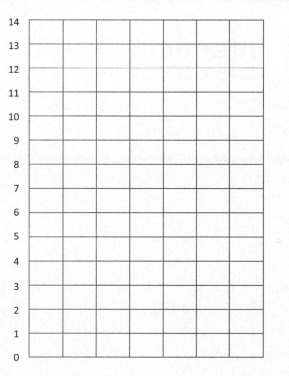

horizontal and vertical bar graphs

EUREKA MATH

Lesson 3:   Draw and label a bar graph to represent data; relate the count scale to the number line.

21

This page intentionally left blank

Name _____ Date _____

1. Complete the bar graph using the table with the types of bugs Alicia counted in the park. Then, answer the following questions.

Types of Bugs			
Butterflies	Spiders	Bees	Grasshoppers
5	14	12	7

Title: _____

0 __ __ __ __ __ __ __ __ __ __ __ __ __

a. How many butterflies were counted in the park? _____

b. How many more bees than grasshoppers were counted in the park? _____

c. Which bug was counted twice as many times as grasshoppers? _____

d. How many bugs did Alicia count in the park? _____

e. How many fewer butterflies than bees and grasshoppers were counted in the park? _____

2. Complete the bar graph with labels and numbers using the number of farm animals on O'Brien's farm.

O'Brien's Farm Animals			
Goats	Pigs	Cows	Chickens
13	15	7	8

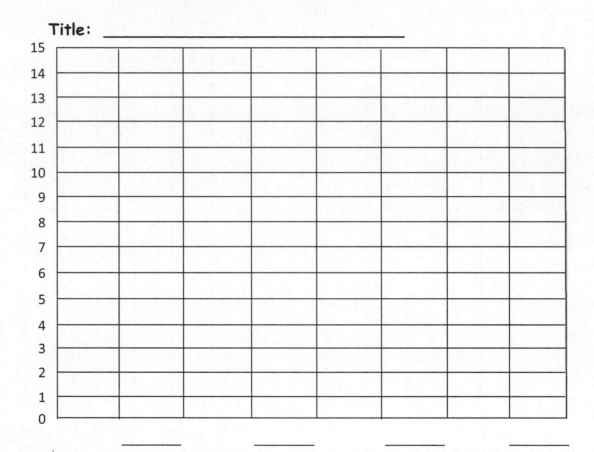

Title: _____

a. How many more pigs than chickens are on O'Brien's farm? _____

b. How many fewer cows than goats are on O'Brien's farm? _____

c. How many fewer chickens than goats and cows are on O'Brien's farm? _____

d. Write a comparison question that can be answered using the data on the bar graph.

_____

Lesson 4:   Draw a bar graph to represent a given data set.

EUREKA MATH

Name _____   Date _____

1. Complete the bar graph using the table with the types of reptiles at the local zoo.
    Then, answer the following questions.

Types of Reptiles			
Snakes	Lizards	Turtles	Tortoises
13	11	7	8

Title: _____

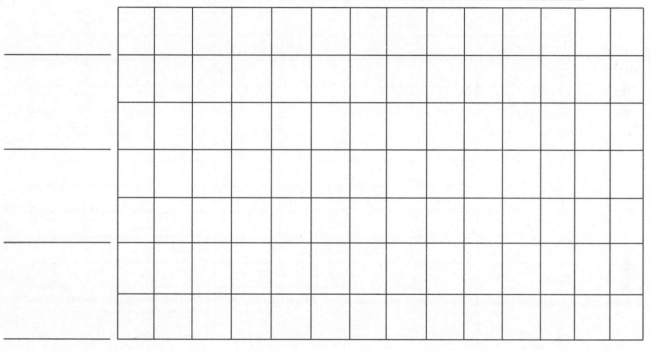

0 __ __ __ __ __ __ __ __ __ __ __ __ __ __

a. How many reptiles are at the zoo? _____

b. How many more snakes and lizards than turtles are at the zoo? _____

c. How many fewer turtles and tortoises than snakes and lizards are at the zoo?
    _____

d. Write a comparison question that can be answered using the data on the bar
    graph.

    _____

©2015 Great Minds. eureka-math.org
G2-M7M8-SE-B4-1.3.1-01.2016

2. Complete the bar graph with labels and numbers using the number of underwater animals Emily saw while scuba diving.

Underwater Animals			
Sharks	Stingrays	Starfish	Seahorses
6	9	14	13

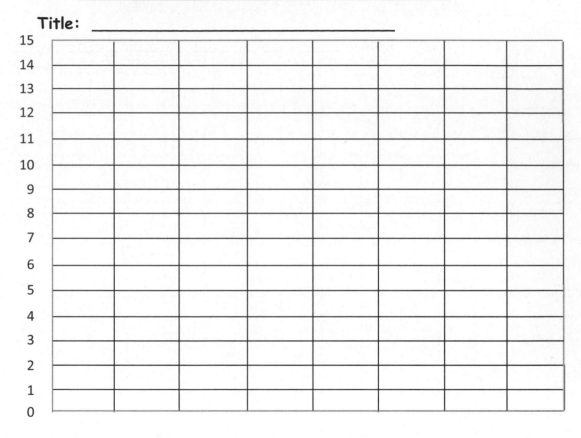

Title: _____

a. How many more starfish than sharks did Emily see? _____

b. How many fewer stingrays than seahorses did Emily see? _____

c. Write a comparison question that can be answered using the data on the bar graph.

_____

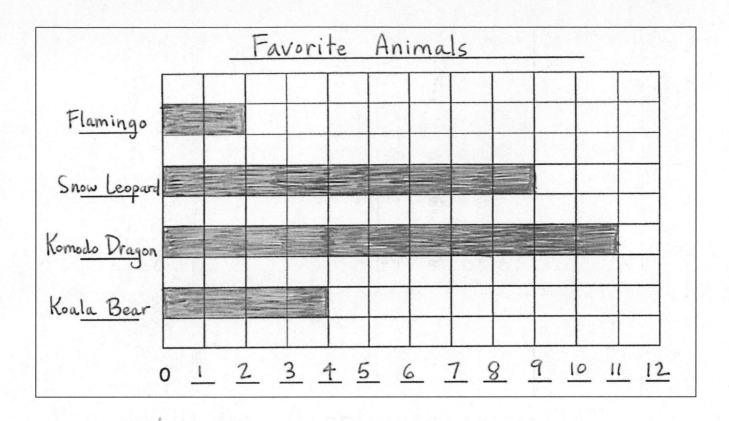

Favorite Animals

	0	1	2	3	4	5	6	7	8	9	10	11	12
Flamingo													
Snow Leopard													
Komodo Dragon													
Koala Bear													

favorite animals bar graph

This page intentionally left blank

Name _____   Date _____

Callista saved pennies. Use the table to complete the bar graph. Then, answer the following questions.

Pennies Saved			
Saturday	Sunday	Monday	Tuesday
15	10	4	7

Title: _____

15							
14							
13							
12							
11							
10							
9							
8							
7							
6							
5							
4							
3							
2							
1							
0							

_____   _____   _____   _____

a. How many pennies did Callista save in all? _____

b. Her sister saved 18 fewer pennies. How many pennies did her sister save? _____

c. How much more money did Callista save on Saturday than on Monday and Tuesday? _____

d. How will the data change if Callista doubles the amount of money she saved on Sunday? _____

e. Write a comparison question that can be answered using the data on the bar graph.
_____

Lesson 5:   Solve word problems using data presented in a bar graph.

29

Name _____   Date _____

A group of friends counted their nickels. Use the table to complete the bar graph.
Then, answer the following questions.

Amount of Nickels			
Annie	Scarlett	Remy	LaShay
5	11	8	14

Title: _____

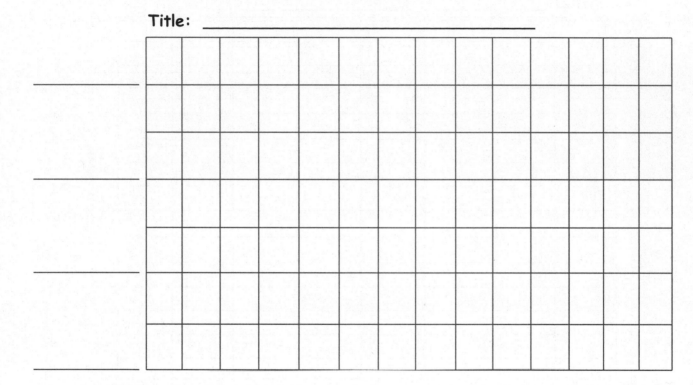

0 __ __ __ __ __ __ __ __ __ __ __ __ __ __

a.   How many nickels do the children have in all? ____

b.   What is the total value of Annie's and Remy's coins? ____

c.   How many fewer nickels does Remy have than LaShay? ____

d.   Who has less money, Annie and Scarlett or Remy and LaShay? _____

e.   Write a comparison question that can be answered using the data on the bar graph.

_____

Lesson 5:   Solve word problems using data presented in a bar graph.

Name _____   Date _____

1. Design a survey, and collect the data.

2. Label and fill in the table.

3. Use the table to label and complete the bar graph.

4. Write questions based on the graph, and then let students use your graphs to answer them.

    a. _____

    b. _____

    c. _____

    d. _____

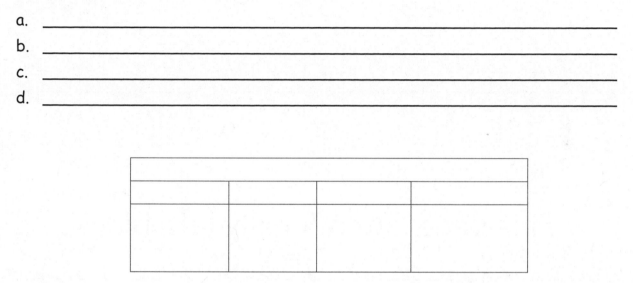

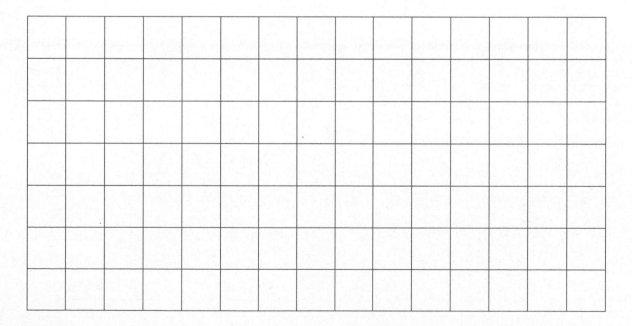

Lesson 5:   Solve word problems using data presented in a bar graph.

31

This page intentionally left blank

Name _____   Date _____

1. Use the table to complete the bar graph. Then, answer the following questions.

Number of Dimes

Emily	Andrew	Thomas	Ava
8	12	6	13

Title: _____

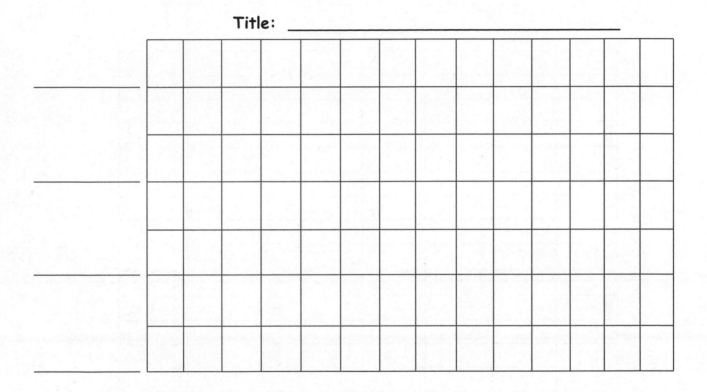

a. How many more dimes does Andrew have than Emily? _____

b. How many fewer dimes does Thomas have than Ava and Emily? _____

c. Circle the pair with more dimes, Emily and Ava or Andrew and Thomas.
    How many more? _____

d. What is the total number of dimes if all the students combine all their money?

    _____

2. Use the table to complete the bar graph. Then, answer the following questions.

Number of Dimes Donated

Madison	Robin	Benjamin	Miguel
12	10	15	13

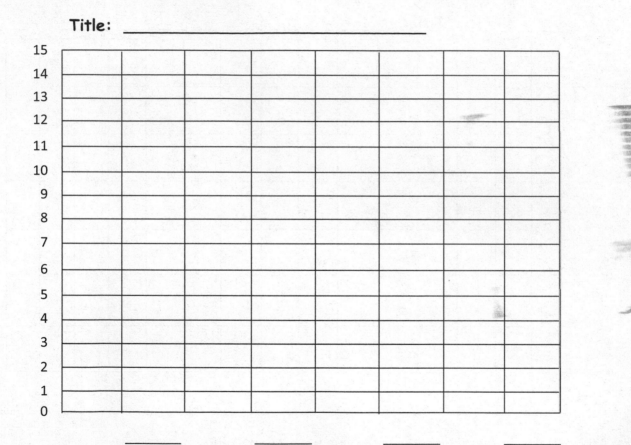

Title: _____

a. How many more dimes did Miguel donate than Robin? _____

b. How many fewer dimes did Madison donate than Robin and Benjamin? _____

c. How many more dimes are needed for Miguel to donate the same as Benjamin and Madison? _____

d. How many dimes were donated? _____

EUREKA MATH

Name _____   Date _____

1. Use the table to complete the bar graph. Then, answer the following questions.

Number of Nickels

Justin	Melissa	Meghan	Douglas
13	9	12	7

Title: _____

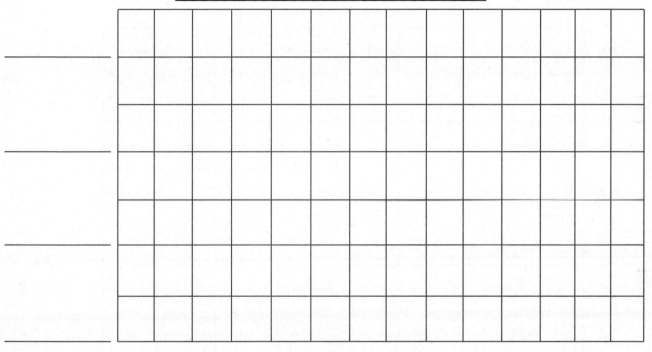

a. How many more nickels does Meghan have than Melissa? _____

b. How many fewer nickels does Douglas have than Justin? _____

c. Circle the pair that has more nickels, Justin and Melissa or Douglas and Meghan. How many more? _____

d. What is the total number of nickels if all the students combine all their money?

_____

EUREKA MATH

Lesson 5:   Solve word problems using data presented in a bar graph.

35

©2015 Great Minds. eureka-math.org
G2-M7M8-SE-B4-1.3.1-01.2016

2. Use the table to complete the bar graph. Then, answer the following questions.

Dimes Donated

Kylie	Tom	John	Shannon
12	10	15	13

Title: _____

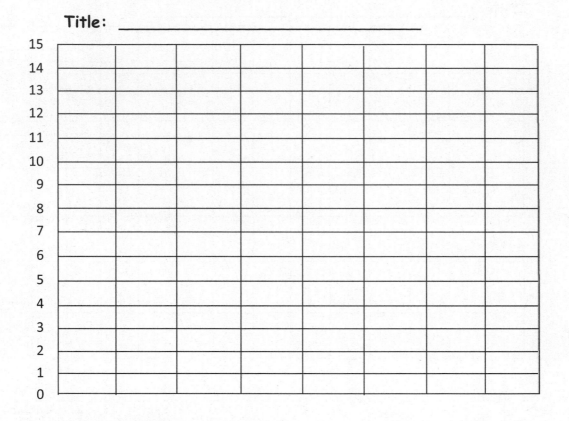

a. How many dimes did Shannon donate? _____

b. How many fewer dimes did Kylie donate than John and Shannon? _____

c. How many more dimes are needed for Tom to donate the same as Shannon and Kylie? _____

d. How many dimes were donated in total? _____

Lesson 5:   Solve word problems using data presented in a bar graph.

Name _____ Date _____

Count or add to find the total value of each group of coins.

Write the value using the ¢ or $ symbol.

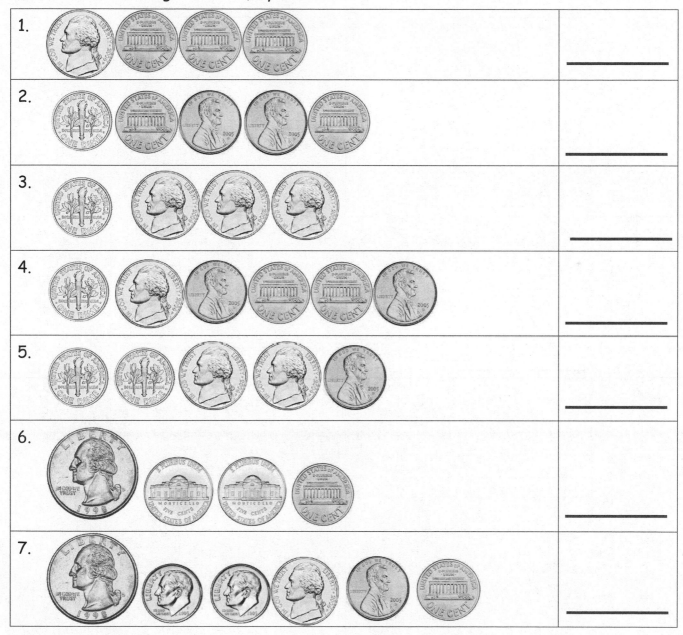

1.

2.

3.

4.

5.

6.

7.

Lesson 6: Recognize the value of coins and count up to find their total value.

37

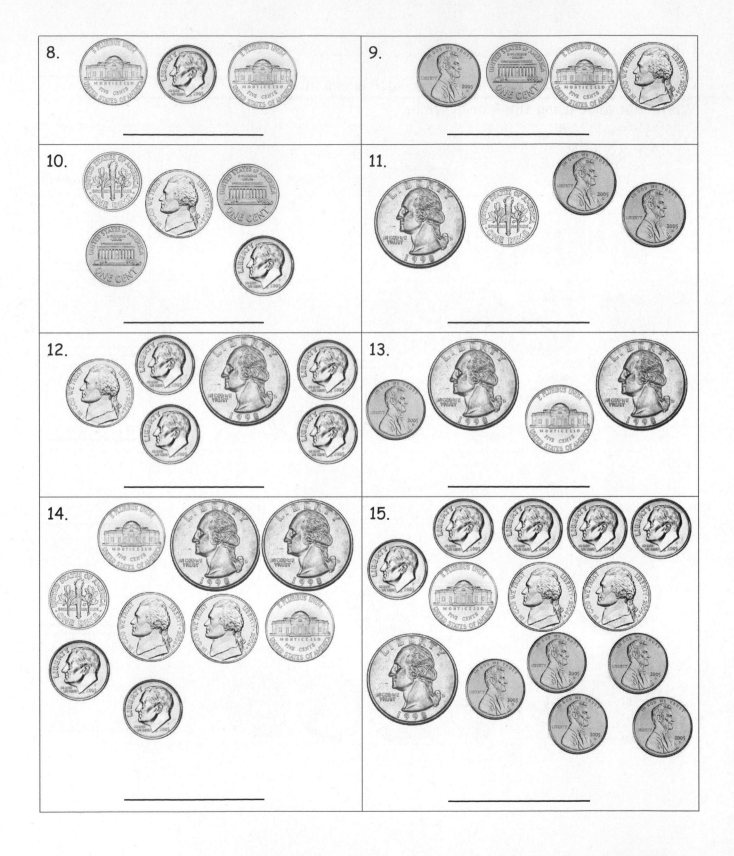

8. _____

9. _____

10. _____

11. _____

12. _____

13. _____

14. _____

15. _____

Lesson 6:   Recognize the value of coins and count up to find their total value.

 EUREKA MATH™

Name _____ Date _____

Count or add to find the total value of each group of coins.
Write the value using the ¢ or $ symbol.

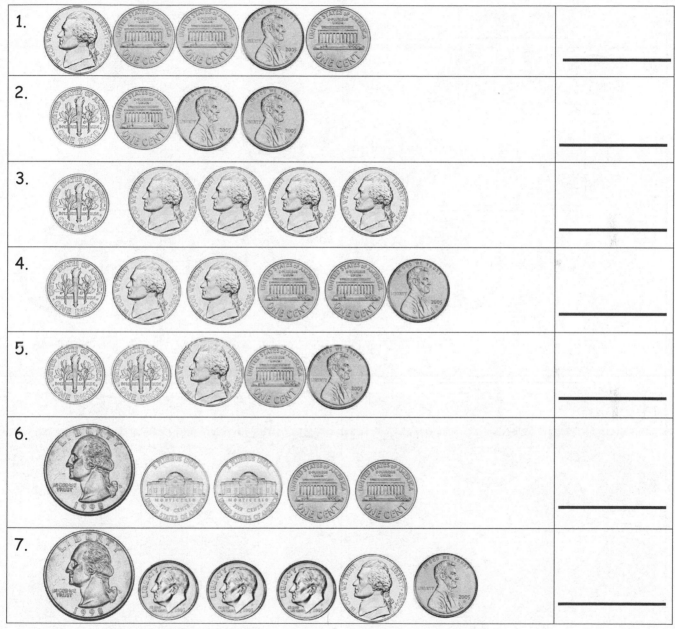

EUREKA
MATH

Lesson 6:   Recognize the value of coins and count up to find their total value.

39

©2015 Great Minds. eureka-math.org
G2-M7M8-SE-B4-1.3.1-01.2016

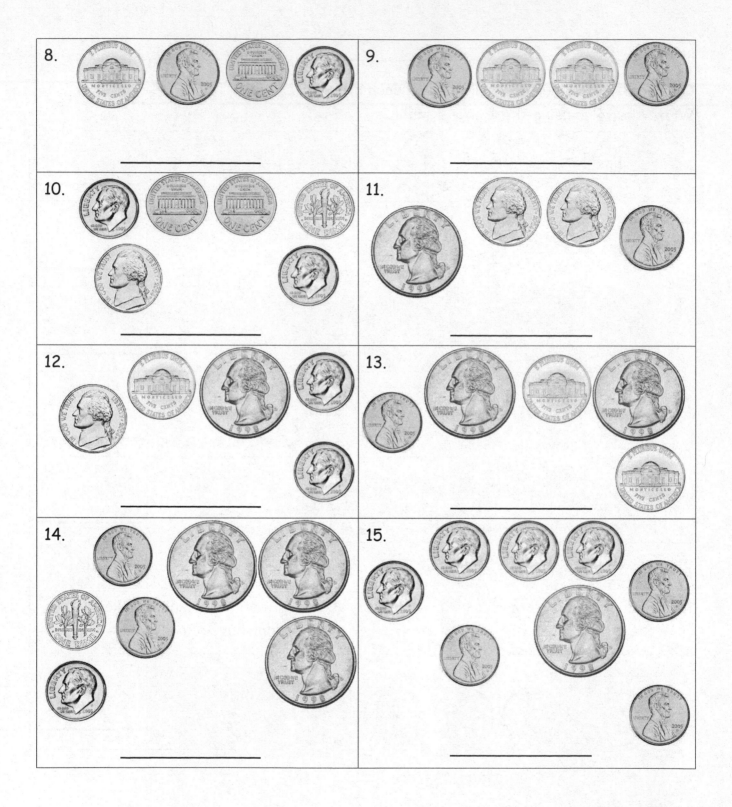

8. _____

9. _____

10. _____

11. _____

12. _____

13. _____

14. _____

15. _____

Lesson 6:   Recognize the value of coins and count up to find their total value.

Name _____ Date _____

Solve.

1. Grace has 3 dimes, 2 nickels, and 12 pennies. How much money does she have?

2. Lisa has 2 dimes and 4 pennies in one pocket and 4 nickels and 1 quarter in the other pocket. How much money does she have in all?

3. Mamadou found 39 cents in the sofa last week. This week, he found 2 nickels, 4 dimes, and 5 pennies. How much money does Mamadou have altogether?

4. Emanuel had 53 cents. He gave 1 dime and 1 nickel to his brother. How much money does Emanuel have left?

5. There are 2 quarters and 14 pennies in the top drawer of the desk and 7 pennies, 2 nickels, and 1 dime in the bottom drawer. What is the total value of the money in both drawers?

6. Ricardo has 3 quarters, 1 dime, 1 nickel, and 4 pennies. He gave 68 cents to his friend. How much money does Ricardo have left?

Lesson 7:   Solve word problems involving the total value of a group of coins.

Name _____   Date _____

Solve.

1. Owen has 4 dimes, 3 nickels, and 16 pennies. How much money does he have?

2. Eli found 1 quarter, 1 dime, and 2 pennies in his desk and 16 pennies and 2 dimes in his backpack. How much money does he have in all?

3. Carrie had 2 dimes, 1 quarter, and 11 pennies in her pocket. Then, she bought a soft pretzel for 35 cents. How much money does Carrie have left?

4. Ethan had 67 cents. He gave 1 quarter and 6 pennies to his sister. How much money does Ethan have left?

5. There are 4 dimes and 3 nickels in Susan's piggy bank. Nevaeh has 17 pennies and 3 nickels in her piggy bank. What is the total value of the money in both piggy banks?

6. Tison had 1 quarter, 4 dimes, 4 nickels, and 5 pennies. He gave 57 cents to his cousin. How much money does Tison have left?

    Lesson 7:   Solve word problems involving the total value of a group of coins.

©2015 Great Minds. eureka-math.org
G2-M7M8-SE-B4-1.3.1-01.2016

Name _____ Date _____

Solve.

1. Patrick has 1 ten-dollar bill, 2 five-dollar bills, and 4 one-dollar bills. How much money does he have?

2. Susan has 2 five-dollar bills and 3 ten-dollar bills in her purse and 11 one-dollar bills in her pocket. How much money does she have in all?

3. Raja has $60. He gave 1 twenty-dollar bill and 3 five-dollar bills to his cousin. How much money does Raja have left?

Lesson 8: Solve word problems involving the total value of a group of bills.

45

4. Michael has 4 ten-dollar bills and 7 five-dollar bills. He has 3 more ten-dollar bills and 2 more five-dollar bills than Tamara. How much money does Tamara have?

5. Antonio had 4 ten-dollar bills, 5 five-dollar bills, and 16 one-dollar bills. He put $70 of that money in his bank account. How much money was not put in his bank account?

6. Mrs. Clark has 8 five-dollar bills and 2 ten-dollar bills in her wallet. She has 1 twenty-dollar bill and 12 one-dollar bills in her purse. How much more money does she have in her wallet than in her purse?

Lesson 8:   Solve word problems involving the total value of a group of bills.

Name _____   Date _____

Solve.

1. Mr. Chang has 4 ten-dollar bills, 3 five-dollar bills, and 6 one-dollar bills. How much money does he have in all?

2. At her yard sale, Danielle got 1 twenty-dollar bill and 5 one-dollar bills last week. This week, she got 3 ten-dollar bills and 3 five-dollar bills. What is the total amount she got for both weeks?

3. Patrick has 2 fewer ten-dollar bills than Brenna. Patrick has $64. How much money does Brenna have?

4. On Saturday, Mary Jo received 5 ten-dollar bills, 4 five-dollar bills, and 17 one-dollar bills. On Sunday, she received 4 ten-dollar bills, 5 five-dollar bills, and 15 one-dollar bills. How much more money did Mary Jo receive on Saturday than on Sunday?

5. Alexis has $95. She has 2 more five-dollar bills, 5 more one-dollar bills, and 2 more ten-dollar bills than Kasai. How much money does Kasai have?

6. Kate had 2 ten-dollar bills, 6 five-dollar bills, and 21 one-dollar bills before she spent $45 on a new outfit. How much money was not spent?

Lesson 8: Solve word problems involving the total value of a group of bills.

Name _____   Date _____

Write another way to make the same total value.

1. 26 cents 2 dimes 1 nickel 1 penny is 26 cents.	Another way to make 26 cents:
2. 35 cents 3 dimes and 1 nickel make 35 cents.	Another way to make 35 cents:
3. 55 cents 2 quarters and 1 nickel make 55 cents.	Another way to make 55 cents:
4. 75 cents The total value of 3 quarters is 75 cents.	Another way to make 75 cents:

EUREKA MATH™

Lesson 9:   Solve word problems involving different combinations of coins with the same total value.

49

©2015 Great Minds. eureka-math.org
G2-M7M8-SE-B4-1.3.1-01.2016

5. Gretchen has 45 cents to buy a yo-yo. Write two coin combinations she could have paid with that would equal 45 cents.

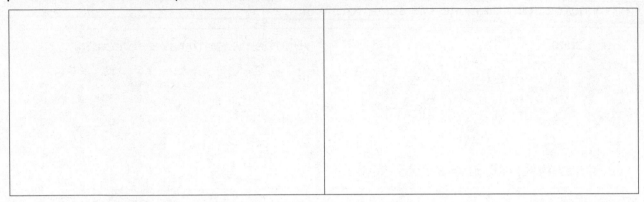

6. The cashier gave Joshua 1 quarter, 3 dimes, and 1 nickel. Write two other coin combinations that would equal the same amount of change.

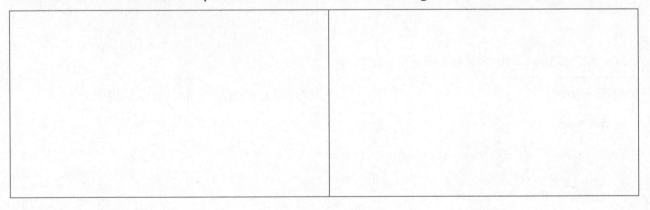

7. Alex has 4 quarters. Nicole and Caleb have the same amount of money. Write two other coin combinations that Nicole and Caleb could have.

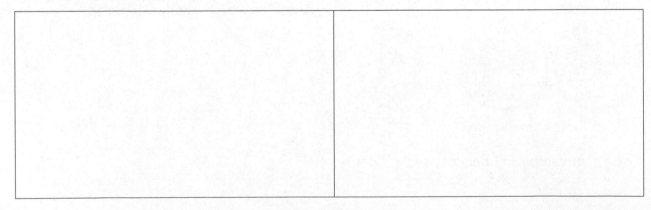

Lesson 9: Solve word problems involving different combinations of coins with the same total value.

Name _____   Date _____

Draw coins to show another way to make the same total value.

1. 25 cents	Another way to make 25 cents:
1 dime 3 nickels is 25 cents.	
2. 40 cents	Another way to make 40 cents:
4 dimes make 40 cents.	
3. 60 cents	Another way to make 60 cents:
2 quarters and 1 dime makes 60 cents.	
4. 80 cents	Another way to make 80 cents:
The total value of 3 quarters 1 nickel is 80 cents.	

EUREKA
MATH™

Lesson 9:   Solve word problems involving different combinations of coins with the
            same total value.

51

©2015 Great Minds. eureka-math.org
G2-M7M8-SE-B4-1.3.1-01.2016

5. Samantha has 67 cents in her pocket. Write two coin combinations she could have that would equal the same amount.

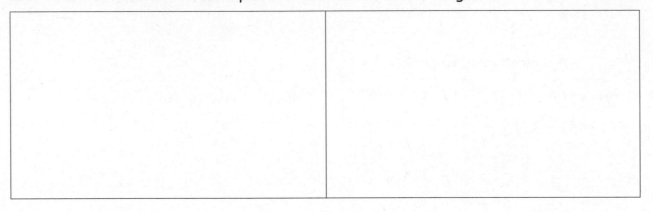

6. The store clerk gave Jeremy 2 quarters, 3 nickels, and 4 pennies. Write two other coin combinations that would equal the same amount of change.

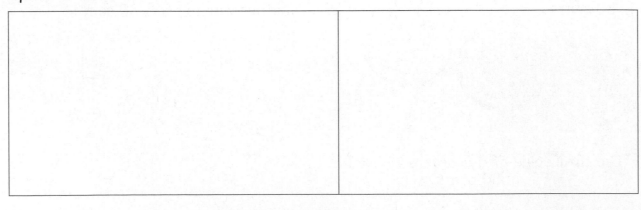

7. Chelsea has 10 dimes. Write two other coin combinations she could have that would equal the same amount.

Lesson 9:   Solve word problems involving different combinations of coins with the same total value.

Name _____ Date _____

1. Kayla showed 30 cents two ways. Circle the way that uses the fewest coins.

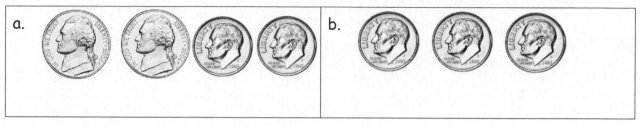

What two coins from (a) were changed for one coin in (b)?

_____

2. Show 20¢ two ways. Use the fewest possible coins on the right below.

	Fewest coins:

3. Show 35¢ two ways. Use the fewest possible coins on the right below.

	Fewest coins:

©2015 Great Minds. eureka-math.org
G2-M7M8-SE-B4-1.3.1-01.2016

4. Show 46¢ two ways. Use the fewest possible coins on the right below.

	Fewest coins:

5. Show 73¢ two ways. Use the fewest possible coins on the right below.

	Fewest coins:

6. Show 85¢ two ways. Use the fewest possible coins on the right below.

	Fewest coins:

7. Kayla gave three ways to make 56¢. Circle the correct ways to make 56¢, and star the way that uses the fewest coins.

   a. 2 quarters and 6 pennies

   b. 5 dimes, 1 nickel, and 1 penny

   c. 4 dimes, 2 nickels, and 1 penny

8. Write a way to make 56¢ that uses the fewest possible coins.

EUREKA MATH™

Name _____   Date _____

1. Tara showed 30 cents two ways. Circle the way that uses the fewest coins.

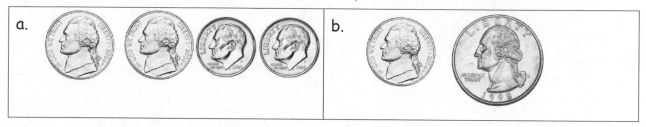

a.

b.

What coins from (a) were changed for one coin in (b)?

_____

2. Show 40¢ two ways. Use the fewest possible coins on the right below.

	Fewest coins:

3. Show 55¢ two ways. Use the fewest possible coins on the right below.

	Fewest coins:

 EUREKA MATH

Lesson 10:   Use the fewest number of coins to make a given value.

55

©2015 Great Minds. eureka-math.org
G2-M7M8-SE-B4-1.3.1-01.2016

4. Show 66¢ two ways. Use the fewest possible coins on the right below.

	Fewest coins:

5. Show 80¢ two ways. Use the fewest possible coins on the right below.

	Fewest coins:

6. Show $1 two ways. Use the fewest possible coins on the right below.

	Fewest coins:

7. Tara made a mistake when asked for two ways to show 91¢. Circle her mistake, and explain what she did wrong.

	Fewest coins:
3 quarters, 1 dime, 1 nickel, and 1 penny	9 dimes and 1 penny

_____

_____

_____

Lesson 10:   Use the fewest number of coins to make a given value.

Name _____   Date _____

1. Count up using the arrow way to complete each number sentence. Then, use your coins to show your answers are correct.

   a. 45¢ + _____ = 100¢

   b. 15¢ + _____ = 100¢

   $$45 \xrightarrow{+5} \underline{\quad} \xrightarrow{+\underline{\quad}} 100$$

   c. 57¢ + _____ = 100¢

   d. _____ + 71¢ = 100¢

2. Solve using the arrow way and a number bond.

   a. 79¢ + _____ = 100¢

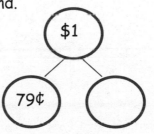

   b. 64¢ + _____ = 100¢

   c. 100¢ – 30¢ = _____

Lesson 11: Use different strategies to make $1 or make change from $1.

57

3. Solve.

a. _____ + 33¢ = 100¢

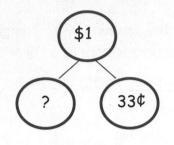

b. 100¢ - 55¢ = _____

c. 100¢ - 28¢ = _____

d. 100¢ - 43¢ = _____

e. 100¢ - 19¢ = _____

Lesson 11:   Use different strategies to make $1 or make change from $1.

Name _____ Date _____

1. Count up using the arrow way to complete each number sentence. Then, use coins to check your answers, if possible.

   a. 25¢ + _____ = 100¢

   b. 45¢ + _____ = 100¢

   $25 \xrightarrow{+5} \underline{\quad} \xrightarrow{+} 100$

   c. 62¢ + _____ = 100¢

   d. _____ + 79¢ = 100¢

2. Solve using the arrow way and a number bond.

   a. 19¢ + _____ = 100¢

   b. 77¢ + _____ = 100¢

   c. 100¢ – 53¢ = _____

EUREKA MATH

Lesson 11:   Use different strategies to make $1 or make change from $1.

59

©2015 Great Minds. eureka-math.org
G2-M7M8-SE-B4-1.3.1-01.2016

3. Solve.

a. _____ + 38¢ = 100¢

b. 100¢ – 65¢ = _____

c. 100¢ – 41¢ = _____

d. 100¢ – 27¢ = _____

e. 100¢ – 14¢ = _____

Lesson 11:   Use different strategies to make $1 or make change from $1.

Name _____   Date _____

Solve using the arrow way, a number bond, or a tape diagram.

1. Jeremy had 80 cents. How much more money does he need to have $1?

2. Abby bought a banana for 35 cents. She gave the cashier $1. How much change did she receive?

3. Joseph spent 75 cents of his dollar at the arcade. How much money does he have left?

4. The notepad Elise wants costs $1. She has 4 dimes and 3 nickels. How much more money does she need to buy the notepad?

5. Dane saved 26 cents on Friday and 35 cents on Monday. How much more money will he need to save to have saved $1?

6. Daniel had exactly $1 in change. He lost 6 dimes and 3 pennies. What coins might he have left?

Lesson 12:   Solve word problems involving different ways to make change from $1.

Name _____ Date _____

Solve using the arrow way, a number bond, or a tape diagram.

1. Kevin had 100 cents. He spent 3 dimes, 3 nickels, and 4 pennies on a balloon.
   How much money does he have left?

2. Colin bought a postcard for 45 cents. He gave the cashier $1. How much change did
   he receive?

3. Eileen spent 75 cents of her dollar at the market. How much money does she have
   left?

EUREKA
MATH™

Lesson 12:   Solve word problems involving different ways to make change from $1.

63

©2015 Great Minds. eureka-math.org
G2-M7M8-SE-B4-1.3.1-01.2016

4. The puzzle Casey wants costs $1. She has 6 nickels, 1 dime, and 11 pennies. How much more money does she need to buy the puzzle?

5. Garret found 19 cents in the sofa and 34 cents under his bed. How much more money will he need to find to have $1?

6. Kelly has 38 fewer cents than Molly. Molly has $1. How much money does Kelly have?

7. Mario has 41 more cents than Ryan. Mario has $1. How much money does Ryan have?

Name _____ Date _____

Solve with a tape diagram and number sentence.

1. Josephine has 3 nickels, 4 dimes, and 12 pennies. Her mother gives her 1 coin.
    Now Josephine has 92 cents. What coin did her mother give her?

2. Christopher has 3 ten-dollar bills, 3 five-dollar bills, and 12 one-dollar bills.
    Jenny has $19 more than Christopher. How much money does Jenny have?

3. Isaiah started with 2 twenty-dollar bills, 4 ten-dollar bills, 1 five-dollar bill, and
    7 one-dollar bills. He spent 73 dollars on clothes. How much money does he have
    left?

EUREKA
MATH™

Lesson 13:   Solve two-step word problems involving dollars or cents with totals
              within $100 or $1.

©2015 Great Minds. eureka-math.org
G2-M7M8-SE-B4-1.3.1-01.2016

65

4. Jackie bought a sweater at the store for $42. She had 3 five-dollar bills and 6 one-dollar bills left over. How much money did she have before buying the sweater?

5. Akio found 18 cents in his pocket. He found 6 more coins in his other pocket. Altogether he has 73 cents. What were the 6 coins he found in his other pocket?

6. Mary found 98 cents in her piggy bank. She counted 1 quarter, 8 pennies, 3 dimes, and some nickels. How many nickels did she count?

Lesson 13:   Solve two-step word problems involving dollars or cents with totals
                                     within $100 or $1.

Name _____   Date _____

1. Kelly bought a pencil sharpener for 47 cents and a pencil for 35 cents. What was her change from $1?

2. Hae Jung bought a pretzel for 3 dimes and a nickel. She also bought a juice box. She spent 92 cents. How much was the juice box?

3. Nolan has 1 quarter, 1 nickel, and 21 pennies. His brother gave him 2 coins. Now he has 86 cents. What 2 coins did his brother give him?

Lesson 13: Solve two-step word problems involving dollars or cents with totals within $100 or $1.

67

4. Monique saved 2 ten-dollar bills, 4 five-dollar bills, and 15 one-dollar bills. Harry saved $16 more than Monique. How much money does Harry have saved?

5. Ryan went shopping with 3 twenty-dollar bills, 3 ten-dollar bills, 1 five-dollar bill, and 9 one-dollar bills. He spent 59 dollars on a video game. How much money does he have left?

6. Heather had 3 ten-dollar bills and 4 five-dollar bills left after buying a new pair of sneakers for $29. How much money did she have before buying the sneakers?

Lesson 13:   Solve two-step word problems involving dollars or cents with totals within $100 or $1.

©2015 Great Minds. eureka-math.org
G2-M7M8-SE-B4-1.3.1-01.2016

Name _____   Date _____

1. Measure the objects below with an inch tile. Record the measurements in the table provided.

Object	Measurement
Pair of scissors	5 in
Marker	5 cm
Pencil	7 in
Eraser	2 in
Length of worksheet	10 in
Width of worksheet	10 in
Length of desk	20 in
Width of desk	20 in

EUREKA
MATH™

Lesson 14:   Connect measurement with physical units by using iteration with an
            inch tile to measure.

69

©2015 Great Minds. eureka-math.org
G2-M7M8-SE-B4-1.3.1-01.2016

2. Mark and Melissa both measured the same marker with an inch tile but came up with different lengths. Circle the student work that is correct, and explain why you chose that work.

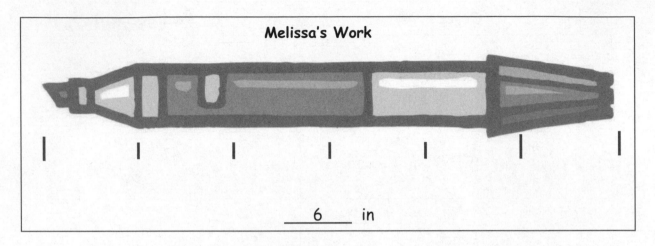

Melissa's Work

_____6_____ in

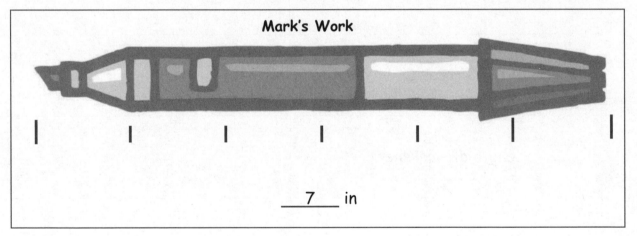

Mark's Work

_____7_____ in

Explanation:

_____

_____

_____

Lesson 14:   Connect measurement with physical units by using iteration with an inch tile to measure.

Name _____   Date _____

1. Measure these objects found in your home with an inch tile. Record the measurements in the table provided.

Object	Measurement
Length of a kitchen fork	
Height of a juice glass	
Length across the center of a plate	
Length of the refrigerator	
Length of a kitchen drawer	
Height of a can	
Length of a picture frame	
Length of a remote control	

Lesson 14: Connect measurement with physical units by using iteration with an inch tile to measure.

71

©2015 Great Minds. eureka-math.org
G2-M7M8-SE-B4-1.3.1-01.2016

2. Norberto begins measuring his pen with his inch tile. He marks off where each tile ends. After two times, he decides this process is taking too long and starts to guess where the tile would end and then marks it.

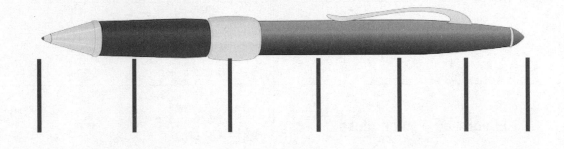

Explain why Norberto's answer will not be correct.

_____

_____

_____

3. Use your inch tile to measure the pen. How many inch tiles long is the pen?

Name _____   Date _____

Use your ruler to measure the length of the objects below in inches. Using your ruler, draw a line that is the same length as each object.

1. a. A pencil is ____7____ inches.

    b. Draw a line that is the same length as the pencil.

2. a. An eraser is ____6____ inches.

    b. Draw a line that is the same length as the eraser.

3. a. A crayon is ____3____ inches.

    b. Draw a line that is the same length as the crayon.

4. a. A marker is ____4____ inches.

    b. Draw a line that is the same length as the marker.

5. a. What is the longest item that you measured? ___pecil___

    b. How long is the longest item? __I MK it 7__ inches

    c. How long is the shortest item? __croyn 3__ inches

    d. What is the difference in length between the longest and the shortest items?

    _____4_____ inches

    e. Draw a line that is the same as the length you found in (d).

EUREKA
MATH™

Lesson 15: Apply concepts to create inch rulers; measure lengths using inch rulers.

73

©2015 Great Minds. eureka-math.org
G2-M7M8-SE-B4-1.3.1-01.2016

6. Measure and label the length of each side of the triangle using your ruler.

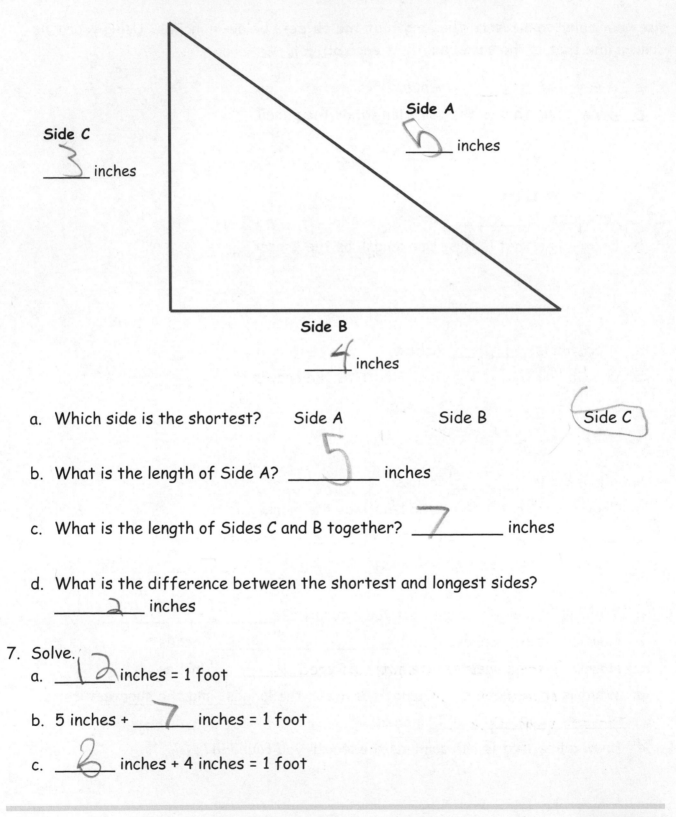

Side A

_5_ inches

Side C

_3_ inches

Side B

_4_ inches

a. Which side is the shortest?   Side A   Side B   (Side C)

b. What is the length of Side A? ____5____ inches

c. What is the length of Sides C and B together? ____7____ inches

d. What is the difference between the shortest and longest sides?
   ____2____ inches

7. Solve.
   a. ___12___ inches = 1 foot

   b. 5 inches + ___7___ inches = 1 foot

   c. ___8___ inches + 4 inches = 1 foot

Lesson 15:   Apply concepts to create inch rulers; measure lengths using inch rulers.

EUREKA MATH

Name _____   Date _____

Measure the length of each household object with your ruler, and then use your ruler to draw a line equal to the length of each object in the space provided.

1. a. A dinner fork is _____ inches.

    b. Draw a line that is the same length as the fork.

2. a. A tablespoon is _____ inches.

    b. Draw a line that is the same length as the tablespoon.

Measure two other household objects.

3. a. _____ is _____ inches.

    b. Draw a line that is the same length as the _____.

4. a. _____ is _____ inches.

    b. Draw a line that is the same length as the _____.

5. a. What was the longest object you measured? _____

    b. What was the shortest object you measured? _____

    c. The difference between the longest object and the shortest object is _____ inches.

Lesson 15:   Apply concepts to create inch rulers; measure lengths using inch rulers.

75

6. Measure and label the length of each side of each shape in inches using your ruler.

5

2

2

a. The longer side of the rectangle is ___5___ inches.

b. The shorter side of the rectangle is ___2___ inches.

c. The longer side of the rectangle is ___2___ inches longer than the shorter side of the rectangle.

d. The shortest side of the trapezoid is ___1___ inches.

e. The longest side of the trapezoid is ___3___ inches.

f. The longest side of the trapezoid is ___6___ inches longer than the shortest side.

g. Each side of the hexagon is ___6___ inches.

h. The total length around the hexagon is ___6___ inches.

| | 1 | 2 | 3 | 4 | 5 |

Center 1: Measure and Compare Shin Lengths

Choose a measuring unit to measure the shins of everyone in your group.
Measure from the top of the foot to the bottom of the knee.

I chose to measure using _____.
Record the results in the table below. Include the units.

Name	Length of Shin

What is the difference in length between the longest and shortest shins? Write a number sentence and statement to show the difference between the two lengths.

Center 2: Compare Lengths to a Yardstick

Fill in your estimate for each object using the words *more than*, *less than*, or *about the same length as*. Then, measure each object with a yardstick, and record the measurement on the chart.

1. The length of a book is

   _____ the yardstick.

2. The height of the door is

   _____ the yardstick.

3. The length of a student desk is

   _____ the yardstick.

Object	Measurement
Length of book	
Height of door	
Length of student desk	

What is the length of 4 student desks pushed together with no gaps in between? Use the RDW process to solve on the back of this paper.

EUREKA MATH

Lesson 16: Measure various objects using inch rulers and yardsticks.

Center 3: Choose the Units to Measure Objects

Name 4 objects in the classroom. Circle which unit you would use to measure each item, and record the measurement in the chart.

Object	Length of the Object
	inches/feet/yards
	inches/feet/yards
	inches/feet/yards
	inches/feet/yards

Billy measures his pencil. He tells his teacher it is 7 feet long. Use the back of this paper to explain how you know that Billy is incorrect and how he can change his answer to be correct.

Center 4: Find Benchmarks

Look around the room to find 2 or 3 objects for each benchmark length. Write each object in the chart, and record the exact length.

Objects That Are About an Inch	Objects That Are About a Foot	Objects That Are About a Yard
1. _____ inches	1. _____ inches	1. _____ inches
2. _____ inches	2. _____ inches	2. _____ inches
3. _____ inches	3. _____ inches	3. _____ inches

Center 5: Choose a Tool to Measure

Circle the tool used to measure each object. Then, measure and record the length in the chart. Circle the unit.

Object	Measurement Tool	Measurement
Length of the rug	12-inch ruler / yardstick	_____ inches/feet
Textbook	12-inch ruler / yardstick	_____ inches/feet
Pencil	12-inch ruler / yardstick	_____ inches/feet
Length of the chalkboard	12-inch ruler / yardstick	_____ inches/feet
Pink eraser	12-inch ruler / yardstick	_____ inches/feet

Sera's jump rope is the length of 6 textbooks. On the back of this paper, make a tape diagram to show the length of Sera's jump rope. Then, write a repeated addition sentence using the textbook measurement from the chart to find the length of Sera's jump rope.

Lesson 16:   Measure various objects using inch rulers and yardsticks.

79

©2015 Great Minds. eureka-math.org
G2-M7M8-SE-B4-1.3.1-01.2016

This page intentionally left blank

Name _____   Date _____

1. Circle the unit that would best measure each object.

Height of a door	inch / foot / yard
Textbook	inch / foot / yard
Pencil	inch / foot / yard
Length of a car	inch / foot / yard
Length of your street	inch / foot / yard
Paint brush	inch / foot / yard

2. Circle the correct estimate for each object.

   a. The height of a flagpole is <u>more than / less than / about the same as</u> the length of a yardstick.

   b. The width of a door is <u>more than / less than / about the same as</u> the length of a yardstick.

   c. The length of a laptop computer is <u>more than / less than / about the same as</u> the length of a 12-inch ruler.

   d. The length of a cell phone is <u>more than / less than / about the same as</u> the length of a 12-inch ruler.

Lesson 16:   Measure various objects using inch rulers and yardsticks.

81

3. Name 3 objects in your classroom. Decide which unit you would use to measure that object. Record it in the chart in a full statement.

Object	Unit
a.	I would use _____ to measure the length of _____.
b.	
c.	

4. Name 3 objects in your home. Decide which unit you would use to measure that object. Record it in the chart in a full statement.

Object	Unit
a.	I would use _____ to measure the length of _____.
b.	
c.	

Lesson 16:   Measure various objects using inch rulers and yardsticks.

EUREKA MATH™

Name _____ Date _____

Estimate the length of each item by using a mental benchmark. Then, measure the item using feet, inches, or yards.

Item	Mental Benchmark	Estimation	Actual Length
a. Width of the door			
b. Width of the white board or chalkboard			
c. Height of a desk			
d. Length of a desk			
e. Length of a reading book			

Lesson 17: Develop estimation strategies by applying prior knowledge of length and using mental benchmarks.

83

Item	Mental Benchmark	Estimation	Actual Length
f. Length of a crayon			
g. Length of the room			
h. Length of a pair of scissors			
i. Length of the window			

Lesson 17:   Develop estimation strategies by applying prior knowledge of length and using mental benchmarks.

EUREKA MATH

Name _____   Date _____

Estimate the length of each item by using a mental benchmark. Then, measure the item using feet, inches, or yards.

Item	Mental Benchmark	Estimation	Actual Length
a. Length of a bed			
b. Width of a bed			
c. Height of a table			
d. Length of a table			
e. Length of a book			

Lesson 17: Develop estimation strategies by applying prior knowledge of length and using mental benchmarks.

85

Item	Mental Benchmark	Estimation	Actual Length
f. Length of your pencil			
g. Length of a refrigerator			
h. Height of a refrigerator			
i. Length of a sofa			

Lesson 17:   Develop estimation strategies by applying prior knowledge of length and using mental benchmarks.

EUREKA MATH™

Name _____   Date _____

Measure the lines in inches and centimeters. Round the measurements to the nearest inch or centimeter.

1. _____

   __12__ cm   __5__ in

2. _____

   __10__ cm   __4__ in

3. _____

   __15__ cm   __5__ in

4. _____

   __8__ cm   __3__ in

5. a. Did you use more inches or more centimeters when measuring the lines above?

   ___cm_____

   b. Write a sentence to explain why you used more of that unit.

   _The spaces for cm_____

   _than in_____

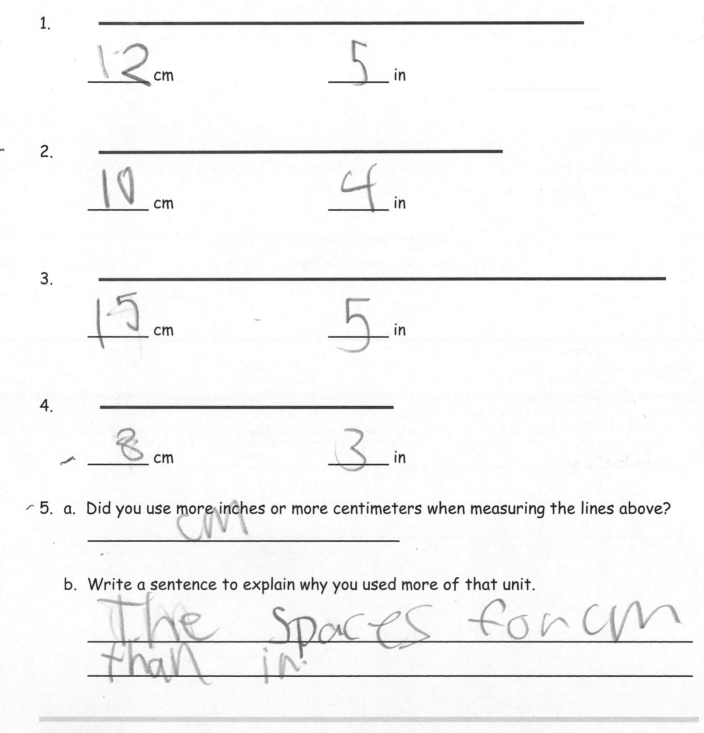

EUREKA
MATH

Lesson 18:   Measure an object twice using different length units and compare;
               relate measurement to unit size.

87

©2015 Great Minds. eureka-math.org
G2-M7M8-SE-B4-1.3.1-01.2016

6. Draw lines with the measurements below.

   a. 3 centimeters long

   b. 3 inches long

7. Thomas and Chris both measured the crayon below but came up with different answers. Explain why both answers are correct.

   Thomas: ___8___ cm
   Chris: ___3___ in

   Explanation: _____

   _____

   _____

   _____

©2015 Great Minds. eureka-math.org
G2-M7M8-SE-B4-1.3.1-01.2016

Name _____   Date _____

Measure the lines in inches and centimeters. Round the measurements to the nearest inch or centimeter.

1. _____

_____ cm   _____ in
  14   6

2. _____

_____ cm   _____ in
  9   4

3. _____

_____ cm   _____ in
  7   3

4. _____

_____ cm   _____ in
  12   4

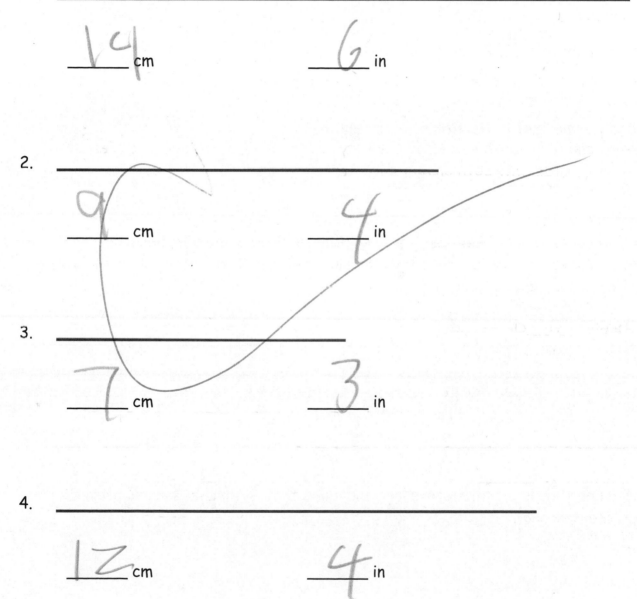

Lesson 18:   Measure an object twice using different length units and compare; relate measurement to unit size.

89

©2015 Great Minds. eureka-math.org
G2-M7M8-SE-B4-1.3.1-01.2016

5. a. Draw a line that is 5 centimeters in length.

    b. Draw a line that is 5 inches in length.

6. a. Draw a line that is 7 inches in length.

    b. Draw a line that is 7 centimeters in length.

7. Takeesha drew a line 9 centimeters long. Damani drew a line 4 inches long.
    Takeesha says her line is longer than Damani's because 9 is greater than 4. Explain
    why Takeesha might be wrong.

    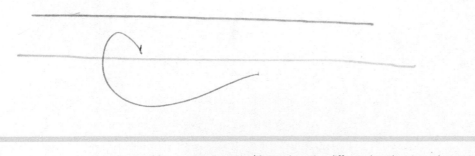

    because in hose spaces
    Takeesha had cm which are smaller than
    inches. is longer

8. Draw a line that is 9 centimeters long and a line that is 4 inches long to prove that
    Takeesha is wrong.

Lesson 18:   Measure an object twice using different length units and compare;
               relate measurement to unit size.

Name _____ Date _____

Measure each set of lines in inches, and write the length on the line. Complete the comparison sentence.

1. Line A _____

   Line B _____

   Line A measured about _____ inches.   Line B measured about _____ inches.

   Line A is about _____ inches **longer** than Line B.

2. Line C   _____

   Line D _____

   Line C measured about _____ inches.   Line D measured about _____ inches.

   Line C is about _____ inches **shorter** than Line D.

Lesson 19:   Measure to compare the differences in lengths using inches, feet, and yards.

91

3. Solve the following problems:

   a. 32 ft + _____ = 87 ft

   b. 68 ft – 29 ft = _____

   c. _____ – 43 ft = 18 ft

4. Tammy and Martha both built fences around their properties. Tammy's fence is 54 yards long. Martha's fence is 29 yards longer than Tammy's.

Tammy's Fence	Martha's Fence
54 yards	_____ yards

   a. How long is Martha's fence? _____ yards

   b. What is the total length of both fences? _____ yards

Lesson 19:   Measure to compare the differences in lengths using inches, feet, and yards.

©2015 Great Minds. eureka-math.org
G2-M7M8-SE-B4-1.3.1-01.2016

Name _____   Date _____

Measure each set of lines in inches, and write the length on the line. Complete the comparison sentence.

1. Line A   _____

    Line B _____

    Line A measured about _____ inches.   Line B measured about _____ inches.

    Line A is about _____ inches **longer** than Line B.

2. Line C   _____

    Line D   _____

    Line C measured about _____ inches.   Line D measured about _____ inches.

    Line D is about _____ inches **shorter** than Line C.

3. Solve. Check your answers with a related addition or subtraction sentence.

    a. 8 inches – 5 inches = _____ inches

        _____ inches + 5 inches = 8 inches

EUREKA MATH   Lesson 19:   Measure to compare the differences in lengths using inches, feet, and   93
                                        yards.

©2015 Great Minds. eureka-math.org
G2-M7M8-SE-B4-1.3.1-01.2016

b. 8 centimeters + _____ centimeters = 19 centimeters

c. 17 centimeters – 8 centimeters = _____ centimeters

d. _____ centimeters + 6 centimeters = 18 centimeters

e. 2 inches + _____ inches = 7 inches

f. 12 inches - _____ = 8 inches

Lesson 19:   Measure to compare the differences in lengths using inches, feet, and yards.

Name _____   Date _____

Solve using tape diagrams. Use a symbol for the unknown.

1. Mr. Ramos has knitted 19 inches of a scarf he wants to be 1 yard long. How many more inches of scarf does he need to knit?

2. In the 100-yard race, Jackie has run 76 yards. How many more yards does she have to run?

3. Frankie has a 64-inch piece of rope and another piece that is 18 inches shorter than the first. What is the total length of both ropes?

EUREKA MATH

Lesson 20:   Solve two-digit addition and subtraction word problems involving length by using tape diagrams and writing equations to represent the problem.

©2015 Great Minds. eureka-math.org
G2-M7M8-SE-B4-1.3.1-01.2016

95

4. Maria had 96 inches of ribbon. She used 36 inches to wrap a small gift and 48 inches to wrap a larger gift. How much ribbon did she have left?

5. The total length of all three sides of a triangle is 96 feet. The triangle has two sides that are the same length. One of the equal sides measures 40 feet. What is the length of the side that is not equal?

?

6. The length of one side of a square is 4 yards. What is the combined length of all four sides of the square?

Lesson 20: Solve two-digit addition and subtraction word problems involving length by using tape diagrams and writing equations to represent the problem.

Name _____   Date _____

Solve using tape diagrams. Use a symbol for the unknown.

1. Luann has a piece of ribbon that is 1 yard long. She cuts off 33 inches to tie a gift box. How many inches of ribbon are not used?

2. Elijah runs 68 yards in a 100-yard race. How many more yards does he have to run?

3. Chris has a 57-inch piece of string and another piece that is 15 inches longer than the first. What is the total length of both strings?

Lesson 20:   Solve two-digit addition and subtraction word problems involving length by using tape diagrams and writing equations to represent the problem.

97

©2015 Great Minds. eureka-math.org
G2-M7M8-SE-B4-1.3.1-01.2016

4. Janine knitted 12 inches of a scarf on Friday and 36 inches on Saturday. She wants the scarf to be 72 inches long. How many more inches does she need to knit?

5. The total length of all three sides of a triangle is 120 feet. Two sides of the triangle are the same length. One of the equal sides measures 50 feet. What is the length of the side that is not equal?

?

6. The length of one side of a square is 3 yards. What is the combined length of all four sides of the square?

Lesson 20:   Solve two-digit addition and subtraction word problems involving
              length by using tape diagrams and writing equations to represent
              the problem.

Name _____ Date _____

Find the value of the point on each part of the meter strip marked by a letter. For each number line, one unit is the distance from one hash mark to the next.

1.

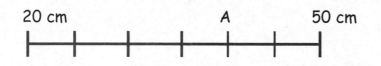

20 cm   A   50 cm

Each unit has a length of _____ centimeters.

A = _____

2.

35 cm   B   85 cm

Each unit has a length of _____ centimeters.

B = _____

3.

C 75 cm   90 cm

Each unit on the meter strip has a length of _____ centimeters.

C = _____

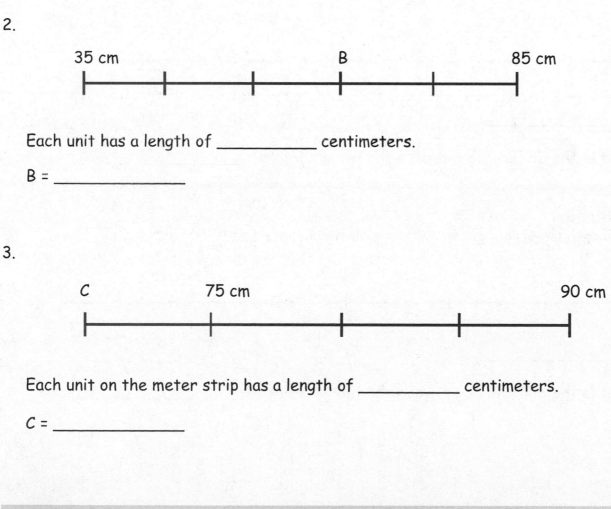

EUREKA MATH™

Lesson 21: Identify unknown numbers on a number line diagram by using the distance between numbers and reference points.

99

4. Each hash mark represents 5 more on the number line.

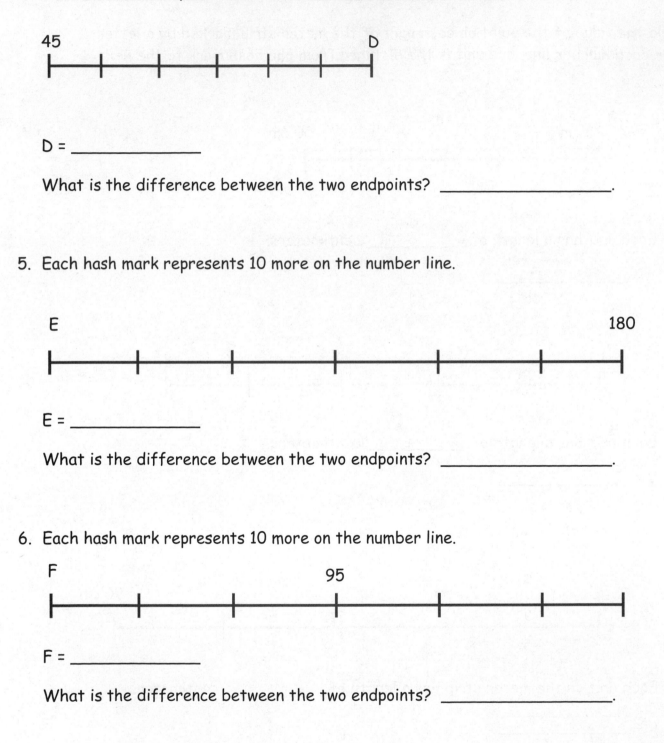

45

D

D = _____

What is the difference between the two endpoints? _____.

5. Each hash mark represents 10 more on the number line.

E

180

E = _____

What is the difference between the two endpoints? _____.

6. Each hash mark represents 10 more on the number line.

F

95

F = _____

What is the difference between the two endpoints? _____.

Lesson 21:   Identify unknown numbers on a number line diagram by using the distance between numbers and reference points.

Name _____ Date _____

Find the value of the point on each part of the meter strip marked by a letter.
For each number line, one unit is the distance from one hash mark to the next.

1.

10 cm ⊢———|———|———A———|———|———| 40 cm

Each unit has a length of _____ centimeters.

A = _____

55 ⊢———|———B———|———|———| 105

Each unit has a length of _____ centimeters.

B = _____

2.

C ⊢———210———|———|———| 240

Each unit has a length of _____ centimeters.

C = _____

EUREKA
MATH

Lesson 21:   Identify unknown numbers on a number line diagram by using the
distance between numbers and reference points.

101

3. Each hash mark represents 5 more on the number line.

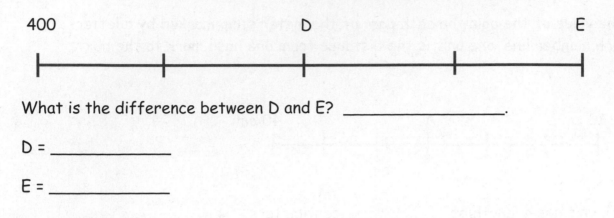

What is the difference between D and E? _____.

D = _____

E = _____

4. Each hash mark represents 10 more on the number line.

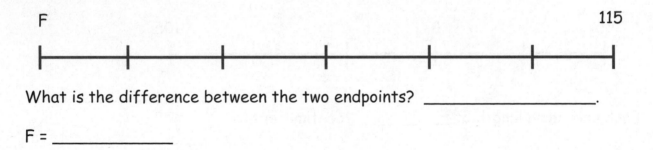

What is the difference between the two endpoints? _____.

F = _____

5. Each hash mark represents 10 more on the number line.

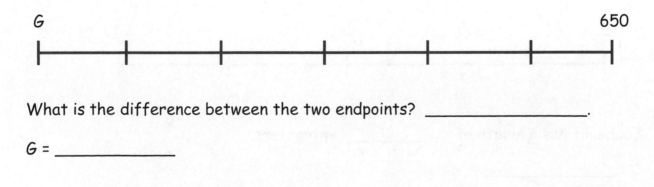

What is the difference between the two endpoints? _____.

G = _____

Lesson 21:   Identify unknown numbers on a number line diagram by using the
distance between numbers and reference points.

Name _____   Date _____

1. Each unit length on both number lines represents 10 centimeters.
   (Note: Number lines are not drawn to scale.)

   a. Show 30 centimeters more than 65 centimeters on the number line.

   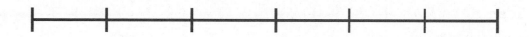

   b. Show 20 centimeters more than 75 centimeters on the number line.

   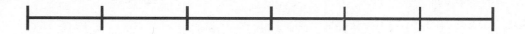

   c. Write an addition sentence to match each number line.

2. Each unit length on both number lines repesents 5 yards.
   a. Show 25 yards less than 90 yards on the following number line.

   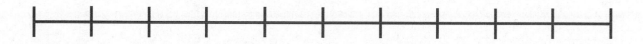

   b. Show 35 yards less than 100 yards on the number line.

   c. Write a subtraction sentence to match each number line.

EUREKA
MATH™

Lesson 22:   Represent two-digit sums and differences involving length by using the
             ruler as a number line.

103

©2015 Great Minds. eureka-math.org
G2-M7M8-SE-B4-1.3.1-01.2016

3. Vincent's meter strip got cut off at 68 centimeters. To measure the length of his screwdriver, he writes "81 cm – 68 cm." Alicia says it's easier to move the screwdriver over 2 centimeters. What is Alicia's subtraction sentence? Explain why she's correct.

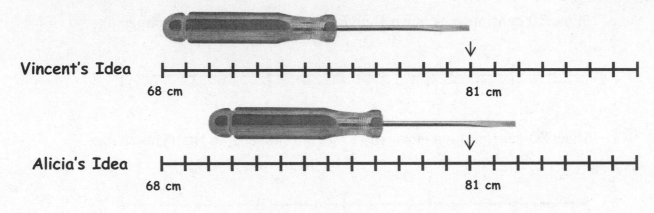

Vincent's Idea

68 cm   81 cm

Alicia's Idea

68 cm   81 cm

4. A large flute is 71 centimeters long, and a small flute is 29 centimeters long. What is the difference between their lengths?

5. Ingrid measured her garden snake's skin to be 28 inches long using a yardstick but didn't start her measurement at zero. What might be the two endpoints of her snakeskin on her yardstick? Write a subtraction sentence to match your idea.

Lesson 22: Represent two-digit sums and differences involving length by using the ruler as a number line.

Name _____   Date _____

1. Each unit length on both number lines represents 10 centimeters.
    (Note: Number lines are not drawn to scale.)

    a. Show 20 centimeters more than 35 centimeters on the number line.

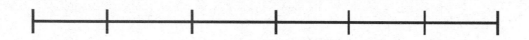

    b. Show 30 centimeters more than 65 centimeters on the number line.

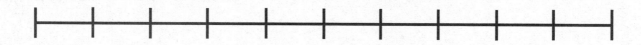

    c. Write an addition sentence to match each number line.

2. Each unit length on both number lines represents 5 yards.

    a. Show 35 yards less than 80 yards on the following number line.

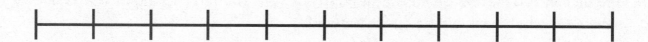

    b. Show 25 yards less than 100 yards on the number line.

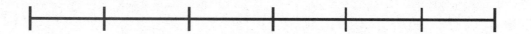

    c. Write a subtraction sentence to match each number line.

Lesson 22:   Represent two-digit sums and differences involving length by using the
             ruler as a number line.

105

©2015 Great Minds. eureka-math.org
G2-M7M8-SE-B4-1.3.1-01.2016

3. Laura's meter strip got cut off at 37 centimeters. To measure the length of her screwdriver, she writes "50 cm – 37 cm." Tam says it's easier to move the screwdriver over 3 centimeters. What is Tam's subtraction sentence? Explain why she's correct.

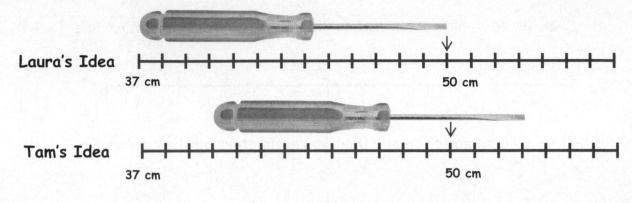

Laura's Idea

37 cm   50 cm

Tam's Idea

37 cm   50 cm

4. Alice measured her belt to be 22 inches long using a yardstick, but she didn't start her measurement at zero. What might be the two endpoints of her belt on her yardstick? Write a subtraction sentence to match your idea.

5. Isaiah ran 100 meters on a 200-meter track. He started running at the 19-meter mark. On what mark did he finish his run?

Number Line A

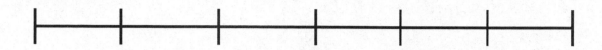

Number Line B

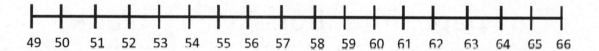

number lines A and B

EUREKA MATH

Lesson 22:   Represent two-digit sums and differences involving length by using the
ruler as a number line.

107

©2015 Great Minds. eureka-math.org
G2-M7M8-SE-B4-1.3.1-01.2016

This page intentionally left blank

Name _____ Date _____

1. Gather and record group data.

   Write your teacher's handspan measurement here: _____

   Measure your handspan, and record the length here: _____

   Measure the handspans of the other people in your group, and write them here. We will be using the data tomorrow.

   Name: **Handspan:**

   _____   _____

   _____   _____

   _____   _____

   _____   _____

   _____   _____

Handspan	Tally of Number of People
3 inches	
4 inches	
5 inches	
6 inches	
7 inches	
8 inches	

What is the most common handspan length? _____

What is the least common handspan length? _____

What do you think the most common handspan length will be for the whole class? Explain why.

_____

_____

_____

_____

_____

Lesson 23: Collect and record measurement data in a table; answer questions and summarize the data set.

109

2. Record the class data.

    Record the class data using tally marks on the table provided.

Handspan	Tally of Number of People
3 inches	
4 inches	
5 inches	
6 inches	
7 inches	
8 inches	

What handspan length is the most common? _____

What handspan length is the least common? _____

Ask and answer a comparison question that can be answered using the data above.

Question: _____

_____

Answer: _____

_____

Lesson 23:   Collect and record measurement data in a table; answer questions and
                      summarize the data set.

©2015 Great Minds. eureka-math.org
G2-M7M8-SE-B4-1.3.1-01.2016

Name _____   Date _____

1. Measure the lines below in inches. Record the data using tally marks on the table provided.

   Line A _____

   Line B _____

   Line C _____

   Line D _____

   Line E _____

   Line F _____

   Line G _____

Line Length	Number of Lines
Shorter than 5 inches	
Longer than 5 inches	
Equal to 5 inches	

2. How many more lines are shorter than 5 inches than are equal to 5 inches?

   _____

3. What is the difference between the number of lines that are shorter than 5 inches and the number that are longer than 5 inches? _____

4. Ask and answer a comparison question that could be answered using the data above.

   Question: _____

   _____

Switch papers with a partner. Have your partner answer your question on the back.

EUREKA MATH™

Lesson 23:   Collect and record measurement data in a table; answer questions and summarize the data set.

111

This page intentionally left blank

Name _____   Date _____

Measure your handspan, and record the length here: _____

Then, measure the handspans of your family members, and write the lengths below.

Name:	Handspan:
_____	_____
_____	_____
_____	_____
_____	_____
_____	_____

1. Record your data using tally marks on the table provided.

Handspan	Tally of Number of People
3 inches	
4 inches	
5 inches	
6 inches	
7 inches	
8 inches	

a. What is the most common handspan length? ____

b. What is the least common handspan length? ____

c. Ask and answer one comparison question that can be answered using the data above.

Question:

_____

_____

Answer:

_____

_____

    Lesson 23:   Collect and record measurement data in a table; answer questions and
summarize the data set.

©2015 Great Minds. eureka-math.org
G2-M7M8-SE-B4-1.3.1-01.2016

113

2. a. Use your ruler to measure the lines below in inches. Record the data using tally marks on the table provided.

Line A _____

Line B _____

Line C _____

Line D _____

Line E _____

Line F _____

Line G _____

Line Length	Number of Lines
Shorter than 4 inches	
Longer than 4 inches	
Equal to 4 inches	

b. How many more lines are shorter than 4 inches than equal to 4 inches?

_____

c. What is the difference between the number of lines that are shorter than 4 inches and those that are longer than 4 inches? _____

d. Ask and answer one comparison question that could be answered using the data above.

Question: _____

_____

Answer: _____

_____

Lesson 23:   Collect and record measurement data in a table; answer questions and summarize the data set.

Name _____   Date _____

Use the data in the tables to create a line plot and answer the questions.

1.

Pencil Length (inches)	Number of Pencils
2	I
3	II
4	⊬ I
5	⊬ II
6	⊬ III
7	IIII
8	I

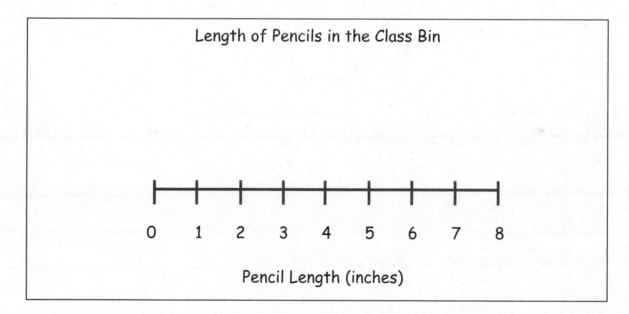

Length of Pencils in the Class Bin

0   1   2   3   4   5   6   7   8

Pencil Length (inches)

Describe the pattern you see in the line plot:

_____

_____

Lesson 24:   Draw a line plot to represent the measurement data; relate the measurement scale to the number line.

115

©2015 Great Minds. eureka-math.org
G2-M7M8-SE-B4-1.3.1-01.2016

2.

Length of Ribbon Scraps (centimeters)	Number of Ribbon Scraps
14	I
16	III
18	‖‖‖ III
20	‖‖‖ II
22	‖‖‖

Scraps of Ribbon in the Arts and Crafts Bin

Line Plot

a. Describe the pattern you see in the line plot.

_____

_____

b. How many ribbons are 18 centimeters or longer? _____

c. How many ribbons are 16 centimeters or shorter? _____

d. Create your own comparison question related to the data.

_____

_____

Lesson 24:   Draw a line plot to represent the measurement data; relate the measurement scale to the number line.

Name _____   Date _____

1. Use the data in the table to create a line plot and answer the question.

Handspan (inches)	Number of Students
2	
3	
4	I
5	ＨＨＴ II
6	ＨＨＴ ＨＨＴ
7	III
8	I

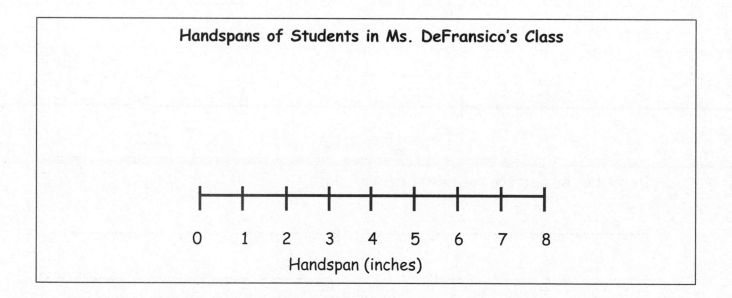

Handspans of Students in Ms. DeFransico's Class

0 1 2 3 4 5 6 7 8
Handspan (inches)

Describe the pattern you see in the line plot:

_____

_____

_____

Lesson 24: Draw a line plot to represent the measurement data; relate the measurement scale to the number line.

117

2. Use the data in the table to create a line plot and answer the questions.

Length of Right Foot (centimeters)	Number of Students
17	I
18	II
19	IIII
20	卌 I
21	卌 I
22	II
23	I

Lengths of Right Feet of Students in Ms. DeFransico's Class

Line Plot

a. Describe the pattern you see in the line plot.

_____

_____

b. How many feet are longer than 20 centimeters? _____

c. How many feet are shorter than 20 centimeters? _____

d. Create your own comparison question related to the data.

_____

Lesson 24:   Draw a line plot to represent the measurement data; relate the measurement scale to the number line.

©2015 Great Minds. eureka-math.org
G2-M7M8-SE-B4-1.3.1-01.2016

Name _____   Date _____

Use the data in the chart provided to create a line plot and answer the questions.

1. The chart shows the heights of the second-grade students in Mr. Yin's homeroom.

Height of Second-Grade Students	Number of Students
40 inches	1
41 inches	2
42 inches	2
43 inches	3
44 inches	4
45 inches	4
46 inches	3
47 inches	2
48 inches	1

Title _____

_____

Line Plot

a. What is the difference between the tallest student and the shortest student?

b. How many students are taller than 44 inches? Shorter than 44 inches?

Lesson 25:   Draw a line plot to represent a given data set; answer questions and draw conclusions based on measurement data.   119

©2015 Great Minds. eureka-math.org
G2-M7M8-SE-B4-1.3.1-01.2016

2. The chart shows the length of paper second-grade students used in their art projects.

Length of Paper	Number of Students
3 ft	2
4 ft	11
5 ft	9
6 ft	6

Title _____

Line Plot

a. How many art projects were made? _____

b. What paper length occurred most often? _____

c. If 8 more students used 5 feet of paper and 6 more students used 6 feet of paper, how would it change how the line plot looks?

_____

_____

d. Draw a conclusion about the data in the line plot.

_____

_____

Draw a line plot to represent a given data set; answer questions and draw conclusions based on measurement data.

Name _____   Date _____

Use the data in the charts provided to create line plots and answer the questions.

1. The chart shows the lengths of the necklaces made in arts and crafts class.

Length of Necklaces	Number of Necklaces
16 inches	3
17 inches	0
18 inches	4
19 inches	0
20 inches	8
21 inches	0
22 inches	9
23 inches	0
24 inches	16

Title _____

Line Plot

a. How many necklaces were made? _____

b. Draw a conclusion about the data in the line plot:

_____

EUREKA MATH

Lesson 25: Draw a line plot to represent a given data set; answer questions and
draw conclusions based on measurement data.

121

©2015 Great Minds. eureka-math.org
G2-M7M8-SE-B4-1.3.1-01.2016

2. The chart shows the heights of towers students made with blocks.

Height of Towers	Number of Towers
15 inches	9
16 inches	6
17 inches	2
18 inches	1

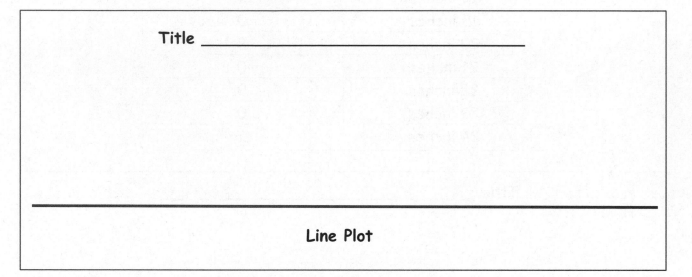

Title _____

Line Plot

a. How many towers were measured? _____

b. What tower height occurred most often? _____

c. If 4 more towers were measured at 17 inches and 5 more towers were measured at 18 inches, how would it change how the line plot looks?

_____

_____

d. Draw a conclusion about the data in the line plot:

_____

_____

Lesson 25:   Draw a line plot to represent a given data set; answer questions and draw conclusions based on measurement data.

Name _____   Date _____

Use the data in the table provided to answer the questions.

1. The table below describes the heights of basketball players and audience members who were polled at a basketball game.

Height (inches)	Number of Participants
25	3
50	4
60	1
68	12
74	18

a. How tall are most of the people who were polled at the basketball game?
_____

b. How many people are 60 inches or taller? _____

c. What do you notice about the people who attended the basketball game?

_____

d. Why would creating a line plot for these data be difficult?

_____

_____

e. For these data, a **line plot / table** (circle one) is easier to read because …

_____

_____

Lesson 26:   Draw a line plot to represent a given data set; answer questions and draw conclusions based on measurement data.

123

©2015 Great Minds. eureka-math.org
G2-M7M8-SE-B4-1.3.1-01.2016

Use the data in the table provided to create a line plot and answer the questions.

2. The table below describes the length of pencils in Mrs. Richie's classroom in centimeters.

Length (centimeters)	Number of Pencils
12	1
13	4
14	9
15	10
16	10

a. How many pencils were measured? _____

b. Draw a conclusion as to why most pencils were 15 and 16 cm:

_____

_____

c. For these data, a **line plot / table** (circle one) is easier to read because...

_____

_____

Lesson 26:   Draw a line plot to represent a given data set; answer questions and
                               draw conclusions based on measurement data.

Name _____ Date _____

Use the data in the table provided to create a line plot and answer the questions. Plot only the lengths of shoelaces given.

1. The table below describes the lengths of student shoelaces in Ms. Henry's class.

Length of Shoelaces (inches)	Number of Shoelaces
27	6
36	10
38	9
40	3
45	2

a. How many shoelaces were measured? _____

b. How many more shoelaces are 27 or 36 inches than 40 or 45 inches? _____

c. Draw a conclusion as to why zero students had a 54-inch shoelace.

_____

2. For these data, a **line plot / table** (circle one) is easier to read because...

_____

Lesson 26:   Draw a line plot to represent a given data set; answer questions and draw conclusions based on measurement data.

125

©2015 Great Minds. eureka-math.org
G2-M7M8-SE-B4-1.3.1-01.2016

Use the data in the table provided to create a line plot and answer the questions.

3. The table below describes the lengths of crayons in centimeters in Ms. Harrison's crayon box.

Length (centimeters)	Number of Crayons
4	4
5	7
6	9
7	3
8	1

a. How many crayons are in the box? _____

b. Draw a conclusion as to why most of the crayons are 5 or 6 centimeters:

_____

_____

_____

Lesson 26:   Draw a line plot to represent a given data set; answer questions and
                                        draw conclusions based on measurement data.

Length of Items in Our Pencil Boxes	Number of Items
6 cm	1
7 cm	2
8 cm	4
9 cm	3
10 cm	6
11 cm	4
13 cm	1
16 cm	3
17 cm	2

Temperatures in May	Number of Days
59°	1
60°	3
63°	3
64°	4
65°	7
67°	5
68°	4
69°	3
72°	1

length and temperature tables

Lesson 26:   Draw a line plot to represent a given data set; answer questions and draw conclusions based on measurement data.

127

©2015 Great Minds. eureka-math.org
G2-M7M8-SE-B4-1.3.1-01.2016

This page intentionally left blank

grid paper

Lesson 26:   Draw a line plot to represent a given data set; answer questions and
draw conclusions based on measurement data.

129

This page intentionally left blank

thermometer

Lesson 26:   Draw a line plot to represent a given data set; answer questions and draw conclusions based on measurement data.   **131**

©2015 Great Minds. eureka-math.org
G2-M7M8-SE-B4-1.3.1-01.2016

This page intentionally left blank

Eureka Math
Grade 2
Module 8

Special thanks go to the Gordon A. Cain Center and to the Department of Mathematics at Louisiana State University for their support in the development of *Eureka Math*.

For a free *Eureka Math* Teacher
Resource Pack, Parent Tip
Sheets, and more please
visit www.Eureka.tools

Published by the non-profit Great Minds™

Copyright © 2015 Great Minds. No part of this work may be reproduced, sold, or commercialized, in whole or in part, without written permission from Great Minds. Non-commercial use is licensed pursuant to a Creative Commons Attribution-NonCommercial-ShareAlike 4.0 license; for more information, go to http://greatminds.net/maps/math/copyright. "Great Minds" and "Eureka Math" are registered trademarks of Great Minds.

Printed in the U.S.A.
This book may be purchased from the publisher at eureka-math.org
10 9 8 7 6 5 4 3

ISBN 978-1-63255-296-9

Name _____   Date _____

1. Identify the number of sides and angles for each shape. Circle each angle as you count, if needed. The first one has been done for you.

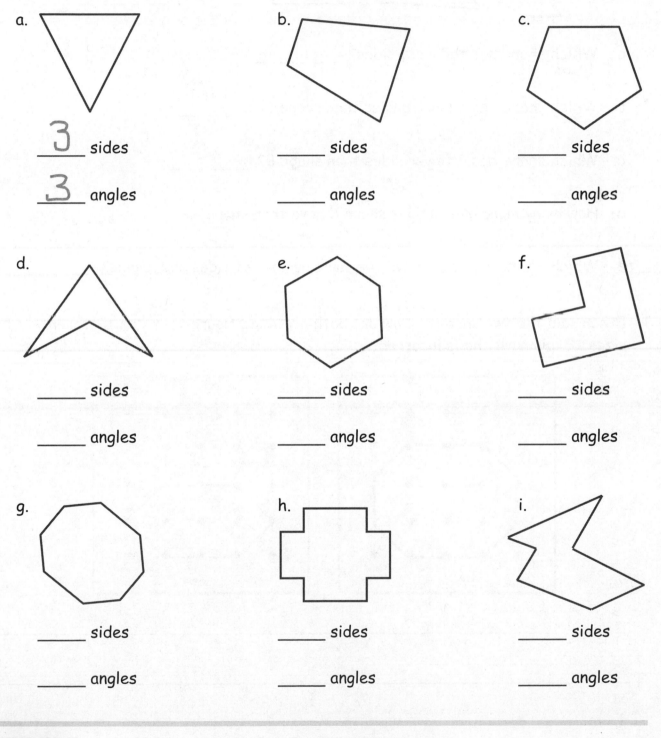

a.

__3__ sides

__3__ angles

b.

_____ sides

_____ angles

c.

_____ sides

_____ angles

d.

_____ sides

_____ angles

e.

_____ sides

_____ angles

f.

_____ sides

_____ angles

g.

_____ sides

_____ angles

h.

_____ sides

_____ angles

i.

_____ sides

_____ angles

2. Study the shapes below. Then, answer the questions.

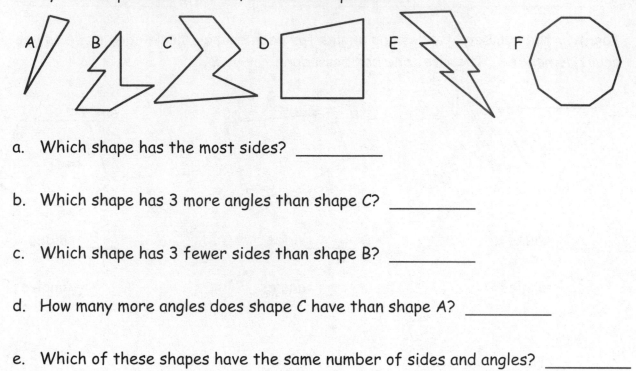

a. Which shape has the most sides? _____

b. Which shape has 3 more angles than shape C? _____

c. Which shape has 3 fewer sides than shape B? _____

d. How many more angles does shape C have than shape A? _____

e. Which of these shapes have the same number of sides and angles? _____

3. Ethan said the two shapes below are both six-sided figures but just different sizes. Explain why he is incorrect.

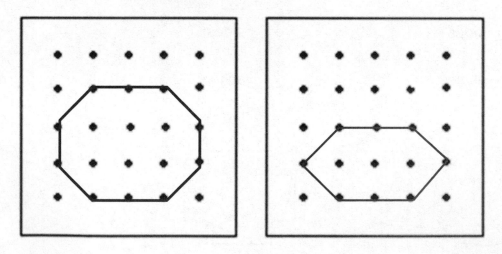

_____

_____

Lesson 1:   Describe two-dimensional shapes based on attributes.

Name _____   Date _____

1. Identify the number of sides and angles for each shape. Circle each angle as you count, if needed.

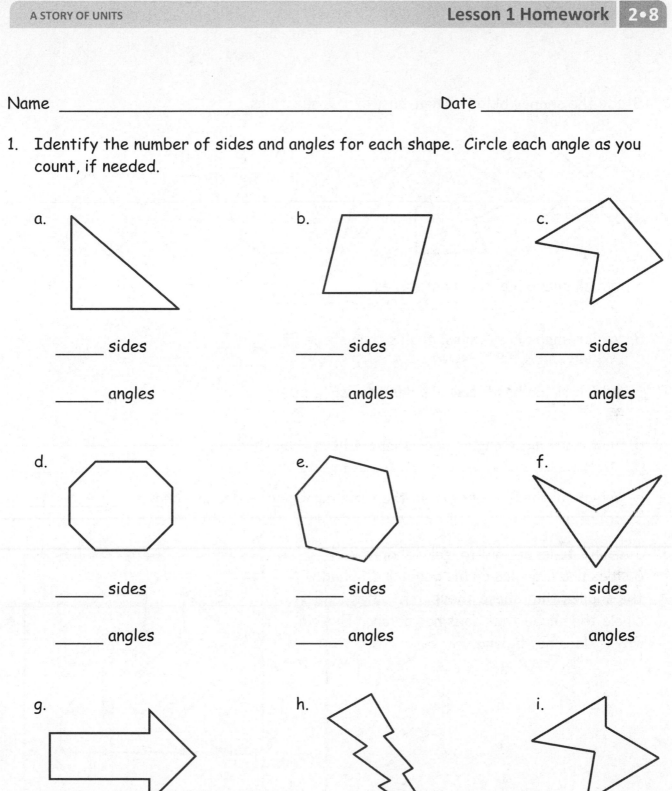

a.

_____ sides

_____ angles

b.

_____ sides

_____ angles

c.

_____ sides

_____ angles

d.

_____ sides

_____ angles

e.

_____ sides

_____ angles

f.

_____ sides

_____ angles

g.

_____ sides

_____ angles

h.

_____ sides

_____ angles

i.

_____ sides

_____ angles

2. Study the shapes below. Then, answer the questions.

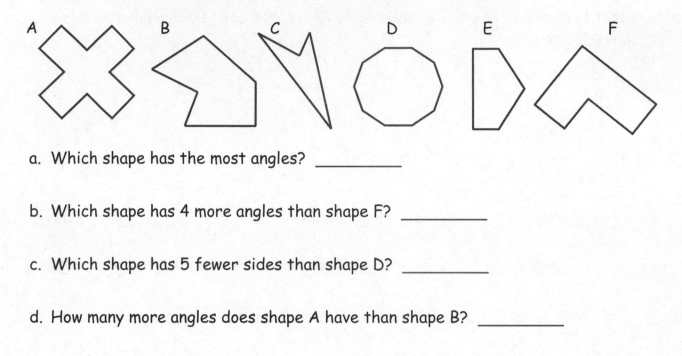

A   B   C   D   E   F

a. Which shape has the most angles? _____

b. Which shape has 4 more angles than shape F? _____

c. Which shape has 5 fewer sides than shape D? _____

d. How many more angles does shape A have than shape B? _____

e. Which of these shapes have the same number of sides and angles? _____

3. Joseph's teacher said to make shapes with
    6 sides and 6 angles on his geoboard. Shade
    the shapes that share these attributes, and
    circle the shape that does not belong. Explain
    why it does not belong.

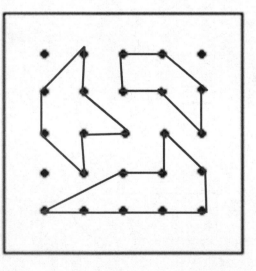

_____

_____

EUREKA
MATH™

Name _____   Date _____

1. Count the number of sides and angles for each shape to identify each polygon. The polygon names in the word bank may be used more than once.

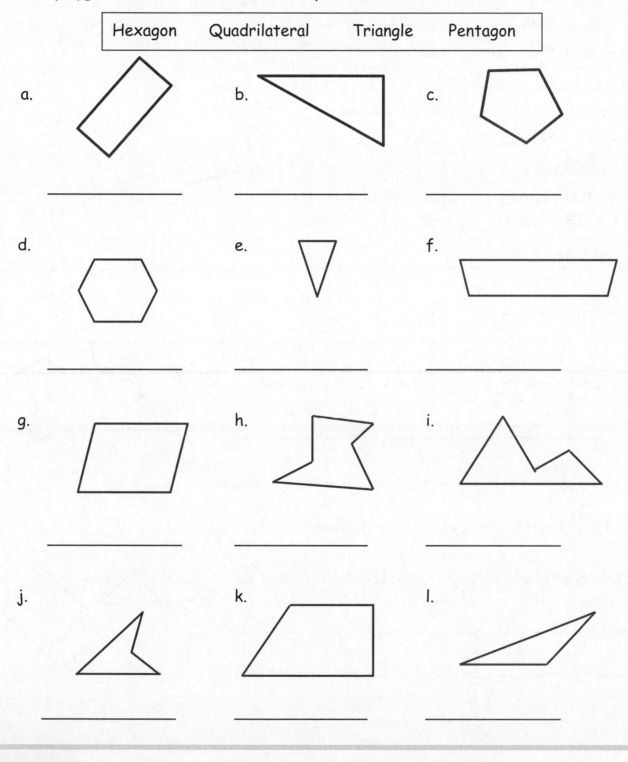

| Hexagon | Quadrilateral | Triangle | Pentagon |

a. _____

b. _____

c. _____

d. _____

e. _____

f. _____

g. _____

h. _____

i. _____

j. _____

k. _____

l. _____

EUREKA MATH™

Lesson 2: Build, identify, and analyze two-dimensional shapes with specified attributes.

5

©2015 Great Minds. eureka-math.org
G2-M7M8-SE-B4-1.3.1-01.2016

2. Draw more sides to complete 2 examples of each polygon.

	Example 1	Example 2
a. **Triangle** For each example, _____ line was added. A triangle has _____ total sides.		
b. **Hexagon** For each example, _____ lines were added. A hexagon has _____ total sides.		
c. **Quadrilateral** For each example, _____ lines were added. A quadrilateral has _____ total sides.		
d. **Pentagon** For each example, _____ lines were added. A pentagon has _____ total sides.		

3.
    a. Explain why both polygons A and B are hexagons.

    _____

    _____

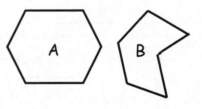

    b. Draw a different hexagon than the two that are shown.

4. Explain why both polygons C and D are quadrilaterals.

    _____

    _____

Name _____ Date _____

1. Count the number of sides and angles for each shape to identify each polygon. The polygon names in the word bank may be used more than once.

| Hexagon | Quadrilateral | Triangle | Pentagon |

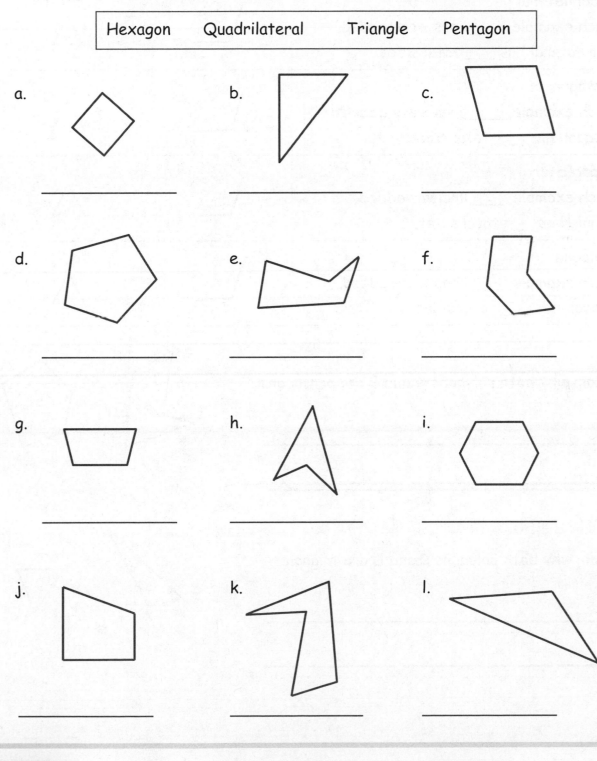

a. _____

b. _____

c. _____

d. _____

e. _____

f. _____

g. _____

h. _____

i. _____

j. _____

k. _____

l. _____

Lesson 2: Build, identify, and analyze two-dimensional shapes with specified attributes.

7

2. Draw more sides to complete 2 examples of each polygon.

	Example 1	Example 2
a. **Quadrilateral** For each example, ____ lines were added. A quadrilateral has ____ total sides.		
b. **Pentagon** For each example, ____ lines were added. A pentagon has ____ total sides.		
c. **Triangle** For each example, ____ line was added. A triangle has ____ total sides.		
d. **Hexagon** For each example, ____ lines were added. A hexagon has ____ total sides.		

3. Explain why both polygons A and B are pentagons.

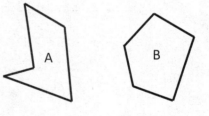

_____

_____

4. Explain why both polygons C and D are triangles.

_____

_____

Lesson 2:   Build, identify, and analyze two-dimensional shapes with specified attributes.

©2015 Great Minds. eureka-math.org
G2-M7M8-SE-B4-1.3.1-01.2016

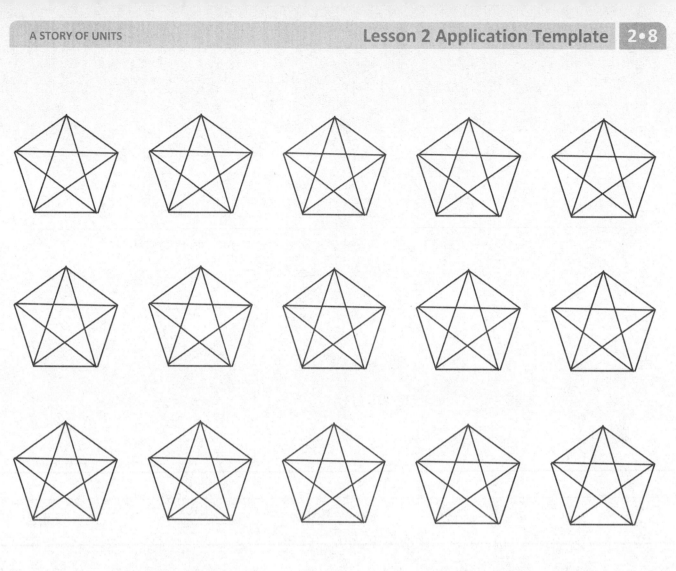

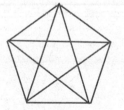 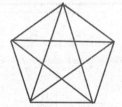 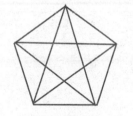 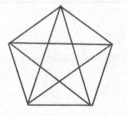 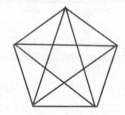

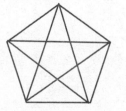 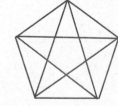 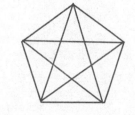 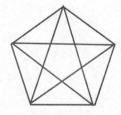 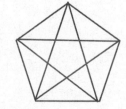

find the triangles

EUREKA MATH™

Lesson 2:   Build, identify, and analyze two-dimensional shapes with specified attributes.

9

find the triangles

Lesson 2:   Build, identify, and analyze two-dimensional shapes with specified attributes.

Name _____ Date _____

1. Use a straightedge to draw the polygon with the given attributes in the space to the right.

   a. Draw a polygon with 3 angles.

       Number of sides: _____

       Name of polygon: _____

   b. Draw a five-sided polygon.

       Number of angles: _____

       Name of polygon: _____

   c. Draw a polygon with 4 angles.

       Number of sides: _____

       Name of polygon: _____

   d. Draw a six-sided polygon.

       Number of angles: _____

       Name of polygon: _____

   e. Compare your polygons to those of your partner.

       Copy one example that is very different from your own in the space to the right.

EUREKA MATH™

Lesson 3:   Use attributes to draw different polygons including triangles, quadrilaterals, pentagons, and hexagons.

11

©2015 Great Minds. eureka-math.org
G2-M7M8-SE-B4-1.3.1-01.2016

2. Use your straightedge to draw 2 new examples of each polygon that are different from those you drew on the first page.

a. Triangle

b. Pentagon

c. Quadrilateral

d. Hexagon

Lesson 3:   Use attributes to draw different polygons including triangles, quadrilaterals, pentagons, and hexagons.

Name _____   Date _____

1. Use a straightedge to draw the polygon with the given attributes in the space to the right.

    a. Draw a polygon with 4 angles.

        Number of sides: _____
        Name of polygon: _____

    b. Draw a six-sided polygon.

        Number of angles: _____
        Name of polygon: _____

    c. Draw a polygon with 3 angles.

        Number of sides: _____
        Name of polygon: _____

    d. Draw a five-sided polygon.

        Number of angles: _____
        Name of polygon: _____

EUREKA MATH™

Lesson 3: Use attributes to draw different polygons including triangles, quadrilaterals, pentagons, and hexagons.

13

©2015 Great Minds. eureka-math.org
G2-M7M8-SE-B4-1.3.1-01.2016

2. Use your straightedge to draw 2 new examples of each polygon that are different from those you drew on the first page.

a. Quadrilateral

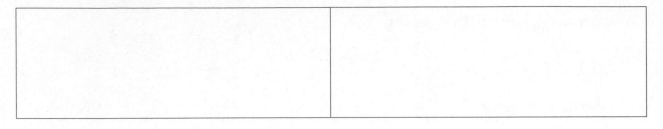

b. Hexagon

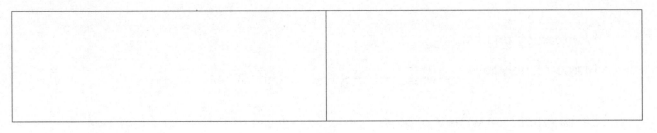

c. Pentagon

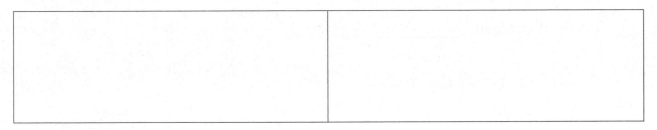

d. Triangle

Lesson 3: Use attributes to draw different polygons including triangles, quadrilaterals, pentagons, and hexagons.

EUREKA
MATH

Name _____   Date _____

1. Use your ruler to draw 2 parallel lines that are not the same length.

2. Use your ruler to draw 2 parallel lines that are the same length.

3. Trace the parallel lines on each quadrilateral using a crayon. For each shape with two sets of parallel lines, use two different colors. Use your index card to find each square corner, and box it.

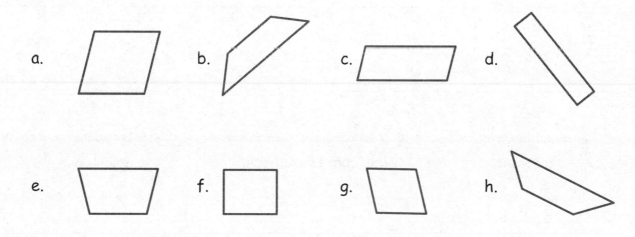

a.

b.

c.

d.

e.

f.

g.

h.

4. Draw a parallelogram with no square corners.

Lesson 4:   Use attributes to identify and draw different quadrilaterals including rectangles, rhombuses, parallelograms, and trapezoids.

15

©2015 Great Minds. eureka-math.org
G2-M7M8-SE-B4-1.3.1-01.2016

5. Draw a quadrilateral with 4 square corners.

6. Measure and label the sides of the figure to the right with your centimeter ruler. What do you notice? Be ready to talk about the attributes of this quadrilateral. Can you remember what this polygon is called?

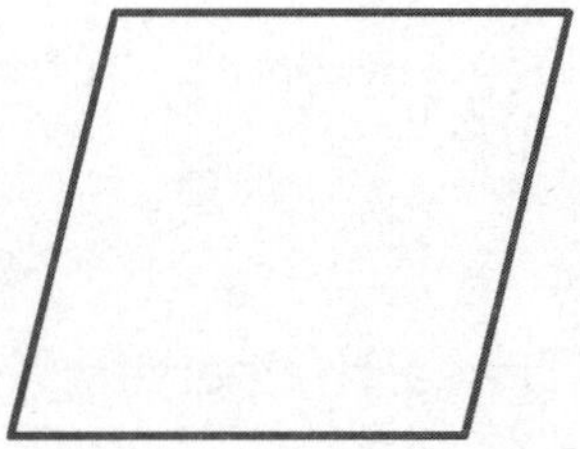

7. A square is a special rectangle. What makes it special?

_____

_____

Lesson 4: Use attributes to identify and draw different quadrilaterals including rectangles, rhombuses, parallelograms, and trapezoids.

Name _____ Date _____

1. Use your ruler to draw 2 parallel lines that are not the same length.

2. Use your ruler to draw 2 parallel lines that are the same length.

3. Draw a quadrilateral with two sets of parallel sides. What is the name of this quadrilateral?

4. Draw a quadrilateral with 4 square corners and opposite sides the same length. What is the name of this quadrilateral?

Lesson 4:   Use attributes to identify and draw different quadrilaterals including rectangles, rhombuses, parallelograms, and trapezoids.

17

©2015 Great Minds. eureka-math.org
G2-M7M8-SE-B4-1.3.1-01.2016

5. A square is a special rectangle. What makes it special?

    _____

    _____

6. Color each quadrilateral with 4 square corners and two sets of parallel sides red.
    Color each quadrilateral with no square corners and no parallel sides blue.
    Circle each quadrilateral with one or more sets of parallel sides green.

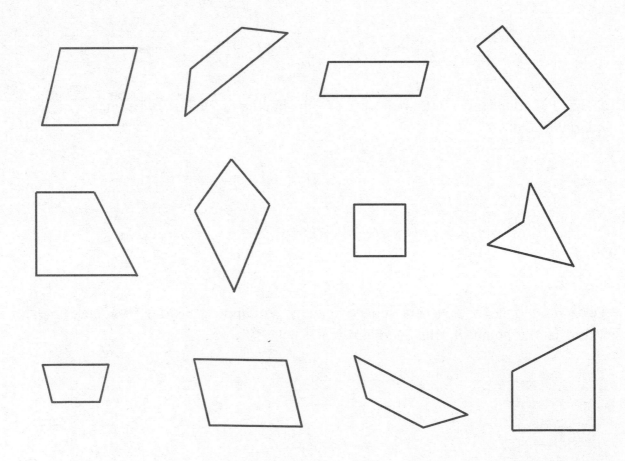

Lesson 4:   Use attributes to identify and draw different quadrilaterals including
rectangles, rhombuses, parallelograms, and trapezoids.

EUREKA
MATH™

Name _____   Date _____

1. Circle the shape that could be the face of a cube.

2. What is the most precise name of the shape you circled? _____

3. How many faces does a cube have? _____

4. How many edges does a cube have? _____

5. How many corners does a cube have? _____

6. Draw 6 cubes, and put a star next to your best one.

First cube	Second cube
Third cube	Fourth cube
Fifth cube	Sixth cube

EUREKA
MATH™

Lesson 5:   Relate the square to the cube, and describe the cube based on attributes.

19

©2015 Great Minds. eureka-math.org
G2-M7M8-SE-B4-1.3.1-01.2016

7. Connect the corners of the squares to make a different kind of drawing of a cube. The first one is done for you.

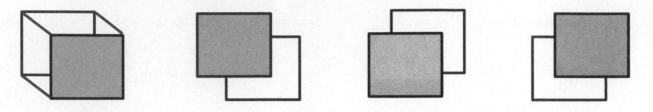

8. Derrick looked at the cube below. He said that a cube only has 3 faces. Explain why Derrick is incorrect.

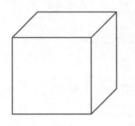

_____

_____

_____

Lesson 5:   Relate the square to the cube, and describe the cube based on attributes.

Name _____   Date _____

1. Circle the shapes that could be the face of a cube.

2. What is the most precise name of the shape you circled? _____

3. How many corners does a cube have? _____

4. How many edges does a cube have? _____

5. How many faces does a cube have? _____

6. Draw 6 cubes, and put a star next to your best one.

First cube	Second cube
Third cube	Fourth cube
Fifth cube	Sixth cube

Lesson 5:   Relate the square to the cube, and describe the cube based on attributes.

21

©2015 Great Minds. eureka-math.org
G2-M7M8-SE-B4-1.3.1-01.2016

7. Connect the corners of the squares to make a different kind of drawing of a cube.

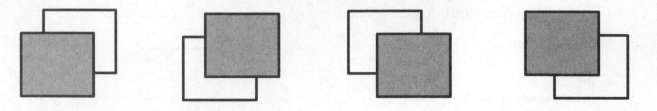

8. Patricia used the image of the cube below to count 7 corners. Explain where the 8th corner is hiding.

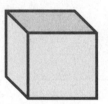

_____

_____

_____

Name _____   Date _____

1. Identify each polygon labeled in the tangram as precisely as possible in the space below.

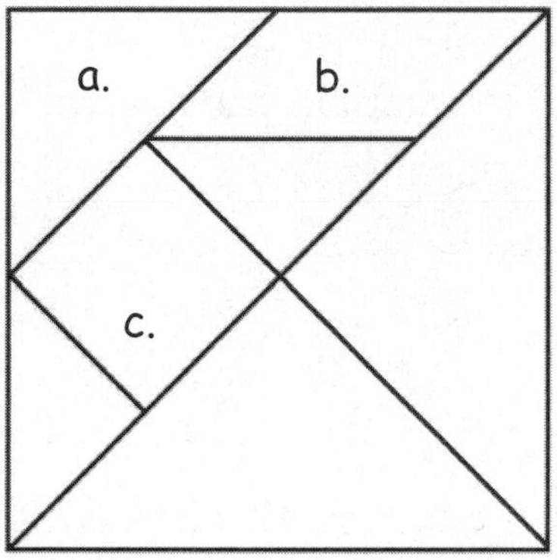

   a. _____

   b. _____

   c. _____

2. Use the square and the two smallest triangles of your tangram pieces to make the following polygons. Draw them in the space provided.

a. A quadrilateral with 1 pair of parallel sides.	b. A quadrilateral with no square corners.
c. A quadrilateral with 4 square corners.	d. A triangle with 1 square corner.

3. Use the parallelogram and the two smallest triangles of your tangram pieces to make the following polygons. Draw them in the space provided.

a. A quadrilateral with 1 pair of parallel sides.	b. A quadrilateral with no square corners.
c. A quadrilateral with 4 square corners.	d. A triangle with 1 square corner.

4. Rearrange the parallelogram and the two smallest triangles to make a hexagon. Draw the new shape below.

5. Rearrange your tangram pieces to make other polygons! Identify them as you work.

Lesson 6:   Combine shapes to create a composite shape; create a new shape from composite shapes.

Name _____   Date _____

1. Identify each polygon labeled in the tangram as precisely as possible in the space below.

   a. _____

   b. _____

   c. _____

2. Use the square and the two smallest triangles of your tangram pieces to make the following polygons. Draw them in the space provided.

a. A triangle with 1 square corner.	b. A quadrilateral with 4 square corners.
c. A quadrilateral with no square corners.	d. A quadrilateral with only 1 pair of parallel sides.

Lesson 6:   Combine shapes to create a composite shape; create a new shape from composite shapes.

25

©2015 Great Minds. eureka-math.org
G2-M7M8-SE-B4-1.3.1-01.2016

3. Rearrange the parallelogram and the two smallest triangles of your tangram pieces to make a hexagon. Draw the new shape below.

4. Rearrange your tangram pieces to make at least 6 other polygons! Draw and name them below.

Lesson 6:   Combine shapes to create a composite shape; create a new shape from composite shapes.

©2015 Great Minds. eureka-math.org
G2-M7M8-SE-B4-1.3.1-01.2016

Cut the tangram into 7 puzzle pieces.

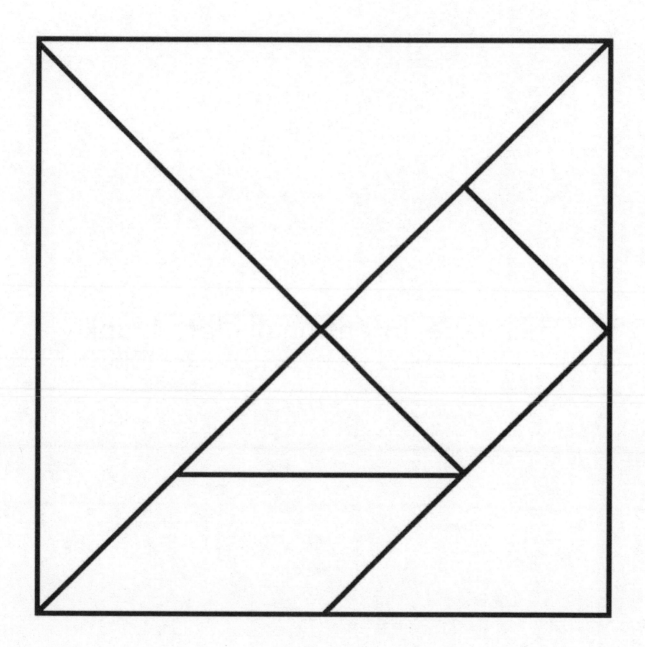

tangram

Lesson 6:   Combine shapes to create a composite shape; create a new shape
from composite shapes.

27

This page intentionally left blank

Name _____   Date _____

1. Solve the following puzzles using your tangram pieces. Draw your solutions in the space below.

a. Use the two smallest triangles to make one larger triangle.	b. Use the two smallest triangles to make a parallelogram with no square corners.
c. Use the two smallest triangles to make a square.	d. Use the two largest triangles to make a square.
e. How many equal shares do the larger shapes in Parts (a–d) have?	f. How many halves make up the larger shapes in Parts (a–d)?

2. Circle the shapes that show halves.

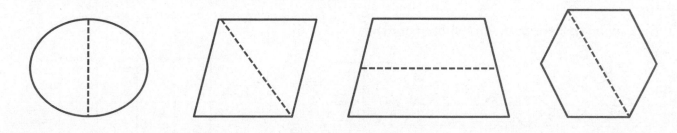

Lesson 7:   Interpret equal shares in composite shapes as halves, thirds, and fourths.

29

©2015 Great Minds. eureka-math.org
G2-M7M8-SE-B4-1.3.1-01.2016

3. Show how 3 triangle pattern blocks form a trapezoid with one pair of parallel lines. Draw the shape below.

a. How many equal shares does the trapezoid have? _____

b. How many thirds are in the trapezoid? _____

4. Circle the shapes that show thirds.

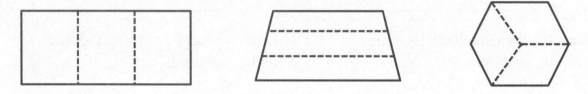

5. Add another triangle to the trapezoid you made in Problem 3 to make a parallelogram. Draw the new shape below.

a. How many equal shares does the shape have now? _____

b. How many fourths are in the shape? _____

6. Circle the shapes that show fourths.

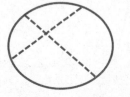 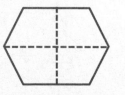 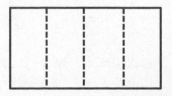

Lesson 7:   Interpret equal shares in composite shapes as halves, thirds, and fourths.

©2015 Great Minds. eureka-math.org
G2-M7M8-SE-B4-1.3.1-01.2016

Name _____   Date _____

1. Solve the following puzzles using your tangram pieces. Draw your solutions in the space below.

a. Use the two largest triangles to make a square.	b. Use the two smallest triangles to make a square.
c. Use the two smallest triangles to make a parallelogram with no square corners.	d. Use the two smallest triangles to make one larger triangle.
e. How many equal shares do the larger shapes in Parts (a–d) have?	f. How many halves make up the larger shapes in Parts (a–d)?

2. Circle the shapes that show halves.

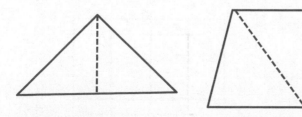 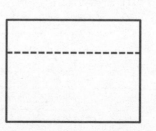 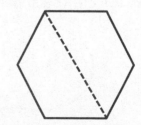

Lesson 7:   Interpret equal shares in composite shapes as halves, thirds, and fourths.

31

©2015 Great Minds. eureka-math.org
G2-M7M8-SE-B4-1.3.1-01.2016

3. Examine the trapezoid.

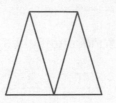

   a. How many equal shares does the trapezoid have? _____

   b. How many thirds are in the trapezoid? _____

4. Circle the shapes that show thirds.

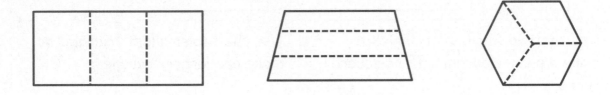

5. Examine the parallelogram.

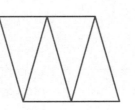

   a. How many equal shares does the shape have? _____

   b. How many fourths are in the shape? _____

6. Circle the shapes that show fourths.

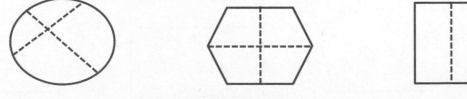

Lesson 7:   Interpret equal shares in composite shapes as halves, thirds, and
              fourths.

Name _____   Date _____

1. Use one pattern block to cover half the rhombus.

   a. Identify the pattern block used to cover half of the rhombus. _____

   b. Draw a picture of the rhombus formed by the 2 halves.

2. Use one pattern block to cover half the hexagon.

   a. Identify the pattern block used to cover half of a hexagon. _____

   b. Draw a picture of the hexagon formed by the 2 halves.

3. Use one pattern block to cover 1 third of the hexagon.

   a. Identify the pattern block used to cover 1 third of a hexagon. _____

   b. Draw a picture of the hexagon formed by the 3 thirds.

4. Use one pattern block to cover 1 third of the trapezoid.

   a. Identify the pattern block used to cover 1 third of a trapezoid. _____

   b. Draw a picture of the trapezoid formed by the 3 thirds.

EUREKA MATH™

Lesson 8:   Interpret equal shares in composite shapes as halves, thirds, and fourths.

33

©2015 Great Minds. eureka-math.org
G2-M7M8-SE-B4-1.3.1-01.2016

5. Use 4 pattern block squares to make one larger square.

    a. Draw a picture of the square formed in the space below.

    b. Shade 1 small square. Each small square is 1 _____ (half / third / fourth) of the whole square.

    c. Shade 1 more small square. Now, 2 _____ (halves / thirds / fourths) of the whole square is shaded.

    d. And 2 fourths of the square is the same as 1 _____ (half / third / fourth) of the whole square.

    e. Shade 2 more small squares. _____ fourths is equal to 1 whole.

6. Use one pattern block to cover 1 sixth of the hexagon.

    a. Identify the pattern block used to cover 1 sixth of a hexagon. _____

    b. Draw a picture of the hexagon formed by the 6 sixths.

Lesson 8:   Interpret equal shares in composite shapes as halves, thirds, and fourths.

©2015 Great Minds. eureka-math.org
G2-M7M8-SE-B4-1.3.1-01.2016

Name _____ Date _____

1. Name the pattern block used to cover half the rhombus. _triangle_

   Sketch the 2 pattern blocks used to cover both halves of the rhombus.

2. Name the pattern block used to cover half the hexagon. _trapezoid_

   Sketch the 2 pattern blocks used to cover both halves of the hexagon.

3. Name the pattern block used to cover 1 third of the hexagon. _rhombus_

   Sketch the 3 pattern blocks used to cover thirds of the hexagon.

4. Name the pattern block used to cover 1 third of the trapezoid. _triangle_

   Sketch the 3 pattern blocks used to cover thirds of the trapezoid.

Lesson 8: Interpret equal shares in composite shapes as halves, thirds, and fourths.

35

©2015 Great Minds. eureka-math.org
G2-M7M8-SE-B4-1.3.1-01.2016

5. Draw 2 lines to make 4 squares in the square below.

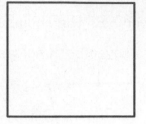

   a. Shade 1 small square. Each small square is 1 _____ (half / third / fourth) of the whole square.

   b. Shade 1 more small square. Now, 2 _____ (halves / thirds / fourths) of the whole square are shaded.

   c. And 2 fourths of the square is the same as 1 _____ (half / third / fourth) of the whole square.

   d. Shade 2 more small squares. _____ fourths is equal to 1 whole.

6. Name the pattern block used to cover 1 sixth of the hexagon. _____
    Sketch the 6 pattern blocks used to cover 6 sixths of the hexagon.

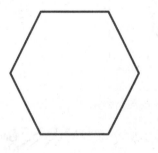

         EUREKA MATH

Name _____   Date _____

1. Circle the shapes that have 2 equal shares with 1 share shaded.

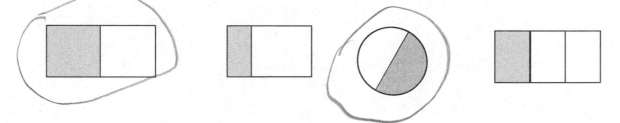

2. Shade 1 half of the shapes that are split into 2 equal shares. One has been done for you.

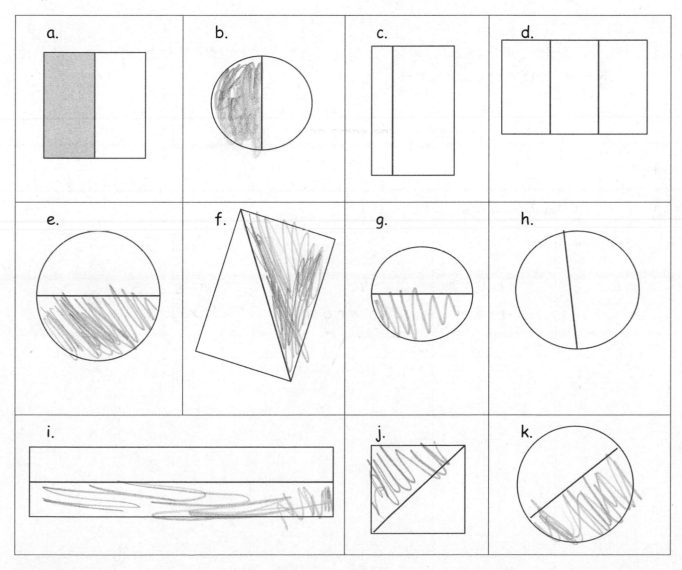

Lesson 9:   Partition circles and rectangles into equal parts, and describe those parts as halves, thirds, or fourths.

37

©2015 Great Minds. eureka-math.org
G2-M7M8-SE-B4-1.3.1-01.2016

3. Partition the shapes to show halves. Shade 1 half of each. Compare your halves to your partner's.

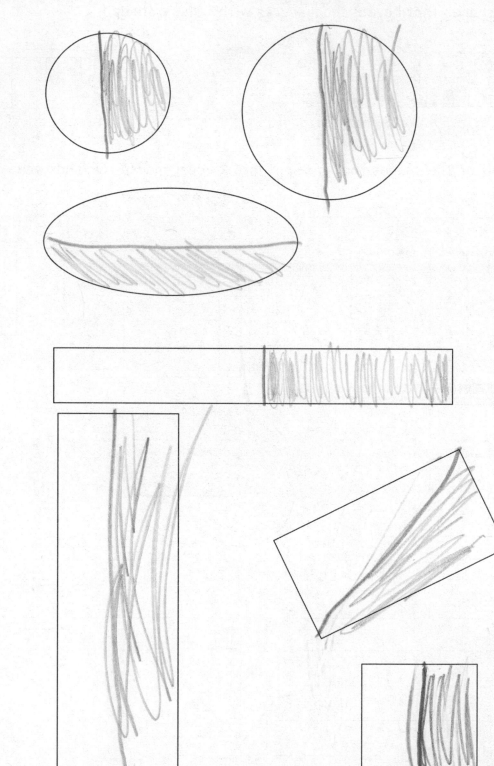

a.

b.

Partition circles and rectangles into equal parts, and describe those
        parts as halves, thirds, or fourths.

©2015 Great Minds. eureka-math.org
G2-M7M8-SE-B4-1.3.1-01.2016

EUREKA
MATH™

Name _____   Date _____

1. Circle the shapes that have 2 equal shares with 1 share shaded.

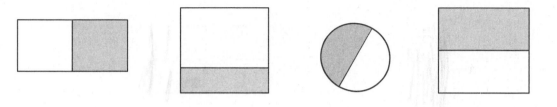

2. Shade 1 half of the shapes that are split into 2 equal shares. One has been done for you.

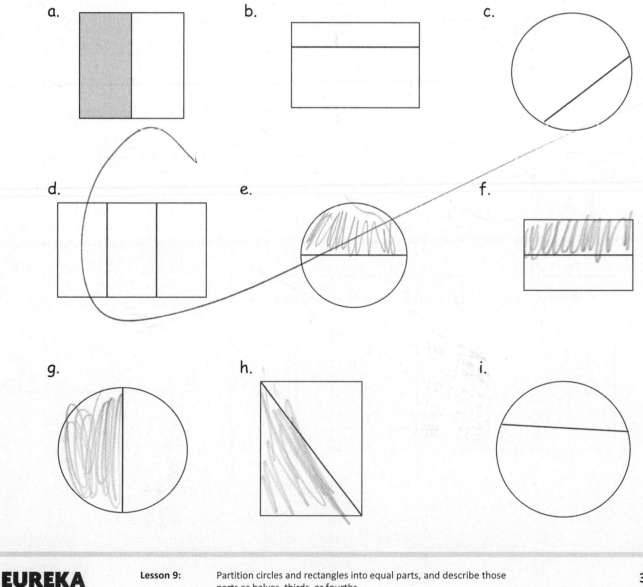

EUREKA MATH   Lesson 9:   Partition circles and rectangles into equal parts, and describe those parts as halves, thirds, or fourths.   39

©2015 Great Minds. eureka-math.org
G2-M7M8-SE-B4-1.3.1-01.2016

3. Partition the shapes to show halves. Shade 1 half of each.

Lesson 9: Partition circles and rectangles into equal parts, and describe those parts as halves, thirds, or fourths.

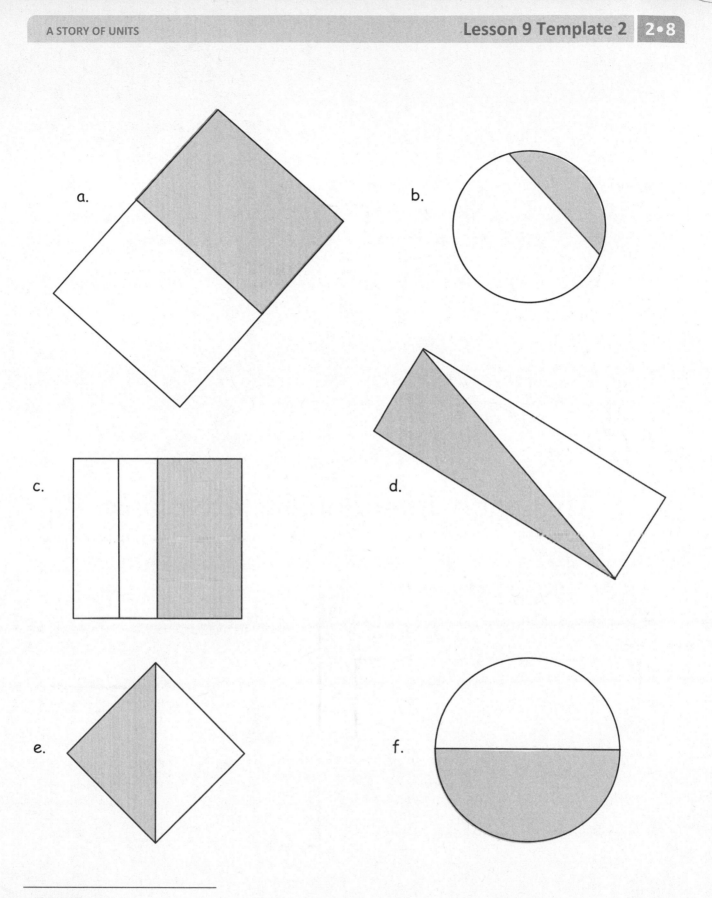

a.

b.

c.

d.

e.

f.

shaded shapes

Lesson 9:   Partition circles and rectangles into equal parts, and describe those parts as halves, thirds, or fourths.

41

©2015 Great Minds. eureka-math.org
G2-M7M8-SE-B4-1.3.1-01.2016

This page intentionally left blank

Name _____   Date _____

1. a. Do the shapes in Problem 1(a) show halves or thirds? ___Halves___

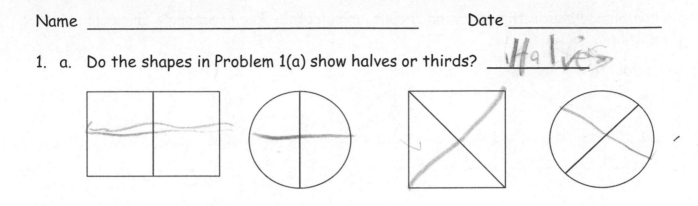

b. Draw 1 more line to partition each shape above into fourths.

2. Partition each rectangle into thirds. Then, shade the shapes as indicated.

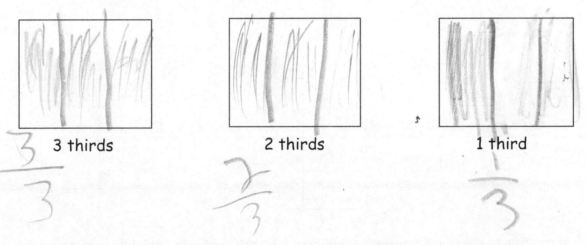

3. Partition each circle into fourths. Then, shade the shapes as indicated.

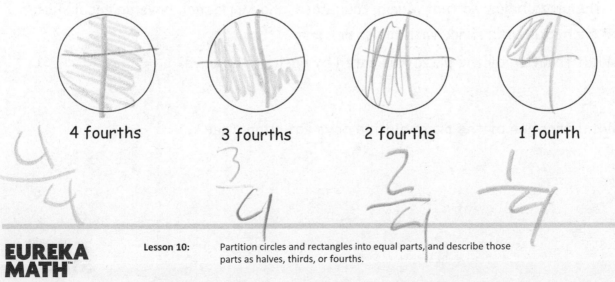

4. Partition and shade the following shapes as indicated. Each rectangle or circle is one whole.

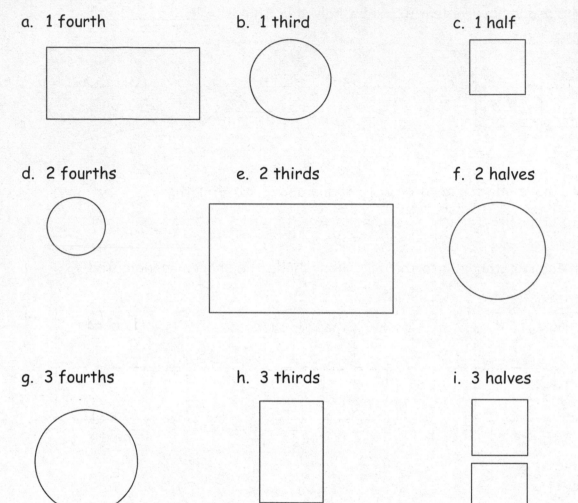

a. 1 fourth

b. 1 third

c. 1 half

d. 2 fourths

e. 2 thirds

f. 2 halves

g. 3 fourths

h. 3 thirds

i. 3 halves

5. Split the pizza below so that Maria, Paul, Jose, and Mark each have an equal share. Label each student's share with his or her name.

a. What fraction of the pizza was eaten by each of the boys?

b. What fraction of the pizza did the boys eat altogether?

Lesson 10:   Partition circles and rectangles into equal parts, and describe those parts as halves, thirds, or fourths.

EUREKA MATH

Name _____   Date _____

1. a. Do the shapes below show halves or thirds? _____

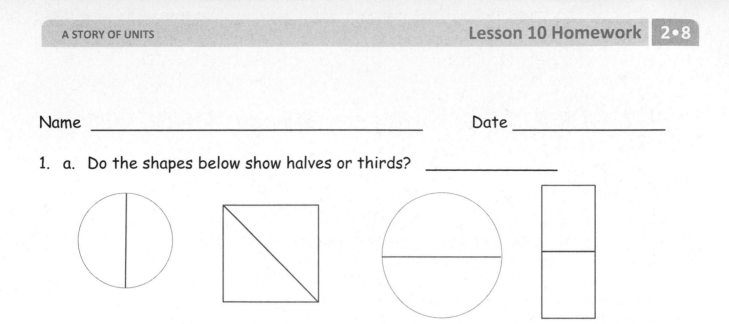

b. Draw 1 more line to partition each shape above into fourths.

2. Partition each rectangle into thirds. Then, shade the shapes as indicated.

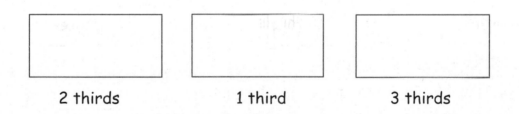

    2 thirds   1 third   3 thirds

3. Partition each circle into fourths. Then, shade the shapes as indicated.

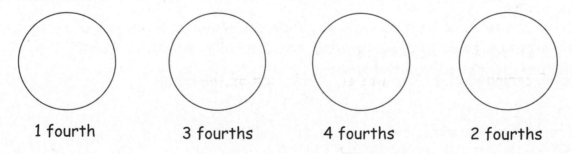

  1 fourth   3 fourths   4 fourths   2 fourths

Lesson 10:   Partition circles and rectangles into equal parts, and describe those
parts as halves, thirds, or fourths.

45

4. Partition and shade the following shapes. Each rectangle or circle is one whole.

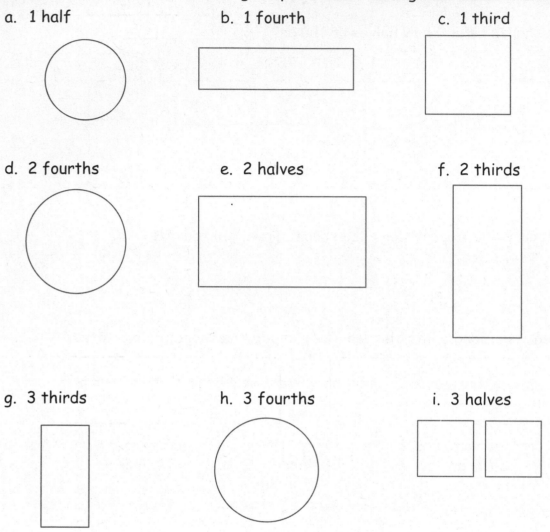

a. 1 half

b. 1 fourth

c. 1 third

d. 2 fourths

e. 2 halves

f. 2 thirds

g. 3 thirds

h. 3 fourths

i. 3 halves

5. Split the pizza below so that Shane, Raul, and John all have an equal share. Label each student's share with his name.

What fraction of the pizza did the boys get in all?

Lesson 10:   Partition circles and rectangles into equal parts, and describe those parts as halves, thirds, or fourths.

EUREKA MATH

rectangles and circles

EUREKA MATH™

Lesson 10: Partition circles and rectangles into equal parts, and describe those parts as halves, thirds, or fourths.

47

©2015 Great Minds. eureka-math.org
G2-M7M8-SE-B4-1.3.1-01.2016

This page intentionally left blank

Name _____   Date _____

1. For Parts (a), (c), and (e), identify the shaded area.

   a.

   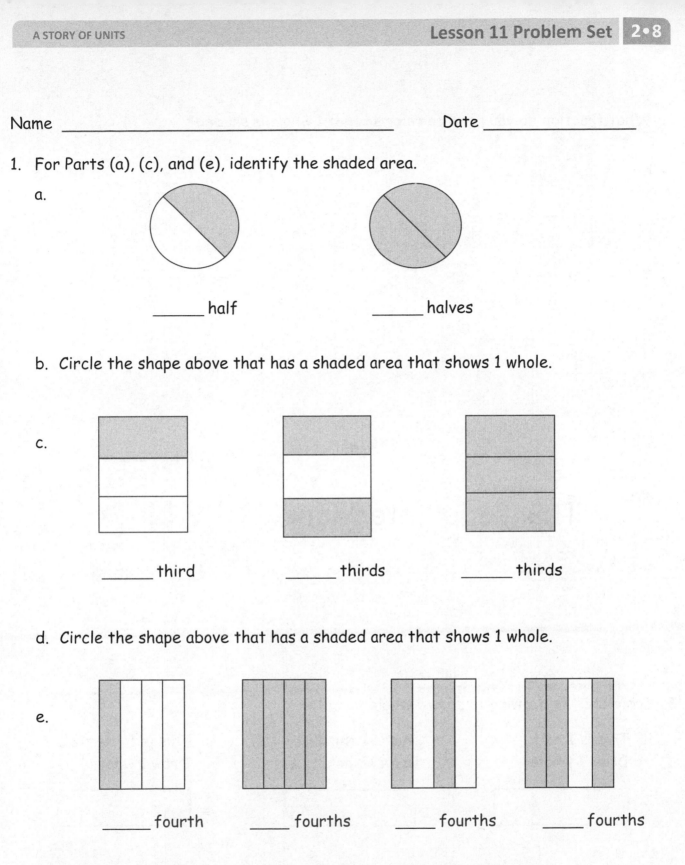

   _____ half   _____ halves

   b. Circle the shape above that has a shaded area that shows 1 whole.

   c.

   _____ third   _____ thirds   _____ thirds

   d. Circle the shape above that has a shaded area that shows 1 whole.

   e.

   _____ fourth   _____ fourths   _____ fourths   _____ fourths

   f. Circle the shape above that has a shaded area that shows 1 whole.

Lesson 11:   Describe a whole by the number of equal parts including 2 halves, 3 thirds, and 4 fourths.

49

2. What fraction do you need to color so that 1 whole is shaded?

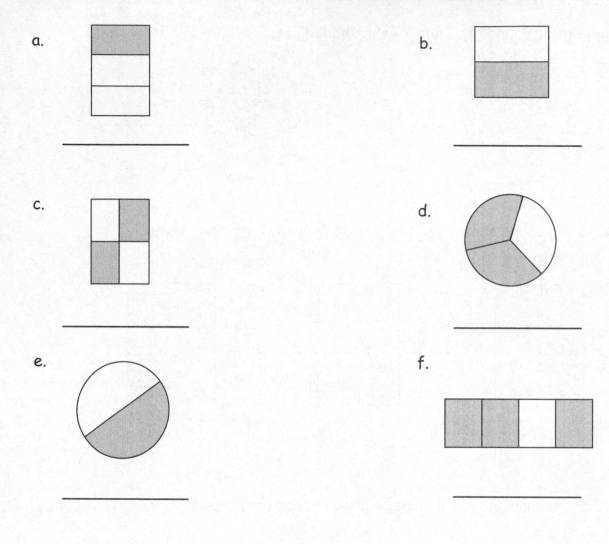

a. _____

b. _____

c. _____

d. _____

e. _____

f. _____

3. Complete the drawing to show 1 whole.

a. This is 1 half.
   Draw 1 whole.

b. This is 1 third.
   Draw 1 whole.

c. This is 1 fourth.
   Draw 1 whole.

Lesson 11:   Describe a whole by the number of equal parts including 2 halves, 3
              thirds, and 4 fourths.

Name _____   Date _____

1. For Parts (a), (c), and (e), identify the shaded area.

   a.

   _____ half   _____ halves

   b. Circle the shape above that has a shaded area that shows 1 whole.

   c.

   _____ third   _____ thirds   _____ thirds

   d. Circle the shape above that has a shaded area that shows 1 whole.

   e.

   _____ fourth   _____ fourths   _____ fourths   _____ fourths

   f. Circle the shape above that has a shaded area that shows 1 whole.

EUREKA MATH™

Lesson 11:   Describe a whole by the number of equal parts including 2 halves, 3
              thirds, and 4 fourths.

51

2. What fraction do you need to color so that 1 whole is shaded?

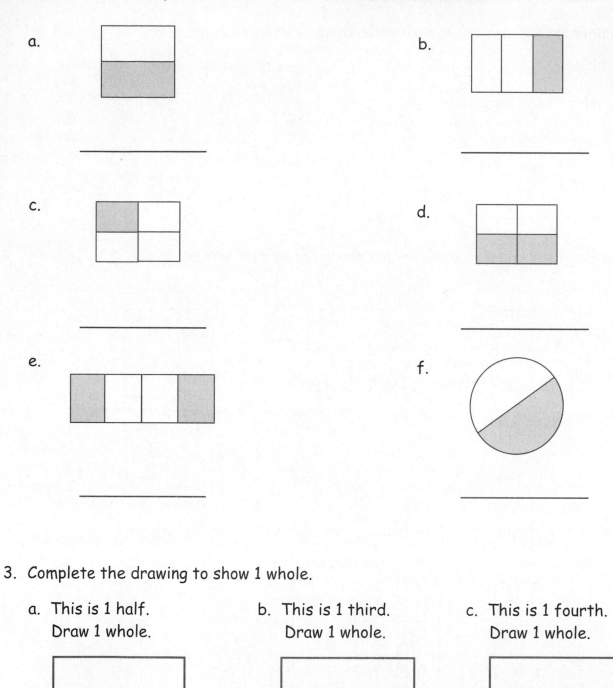

a.

_____

b.

_____

c.

_____

d.

_____

e.

_____

f.

_____

3. Complete the drawing to show 1 whole.

a. This is 1 half.
   Draw 1 whole.

b. This is 1 third.
   Draw 1 whole.

c. This is 1 fourth.
   Draw 1 whole.

Lesson 11:   Describe a whole by the number of equal parts including 2 halves, 3 thirds, and 4 fourths.

©2015 Great Minds. eureka-math.org
G2-M7M8-SE-B4-1.3.1-01.2016

EUREKA
MATH

Name _____   Date _____

1. Partition the rectangles in 2 different ways to show equal shares.

    a. 2 halves

    b. 3 thirds

    c. 4 fourths

2. Build the original whole square using the rectangle half and the half represented by your 4 small triangles. Draw it in the space below.

Lesson 12:   Recognize that equal parts of an identical rectangle can have different shapes.

53

©2015 Great Minds. eureka-math.org
G2-M7M8-SE-B4-1.3.1-01.2016

3. Use different-colored halves of a whole square.

   a. Cut the square in half to make 2 equal-size rectangles.

   b. Rearrange the halves to create a new rectangle with no gaps or overlaps.

   c. Cut each equal part in half to make 4 equal-size squares.

   d. Rearrange the new equal shares to create different polygons.

   e. Draw one of your new polygons from Part (d) below.

Extension

4. Cut out the circle.

   a. Cut the circle in half.

   b. Rearrange the halves to create a new shape with no gaps or overlaps.

   c. Cut each equal share in half.

   d. Rearrange the equal shares to create a new shape with no gaps or overlaps.

   e. Draw your new shape from Part (d) below.

Lesson 12: Recognize that equal parts of an identical rectangle can have different shapes.

©2015 Great Minds. eureka-math.org
G2-M7M8-SE-B4-1.3.1-01.2016

Name _____   Date _____

1. Partition the rectangles in 2 different ways to show equal shares.

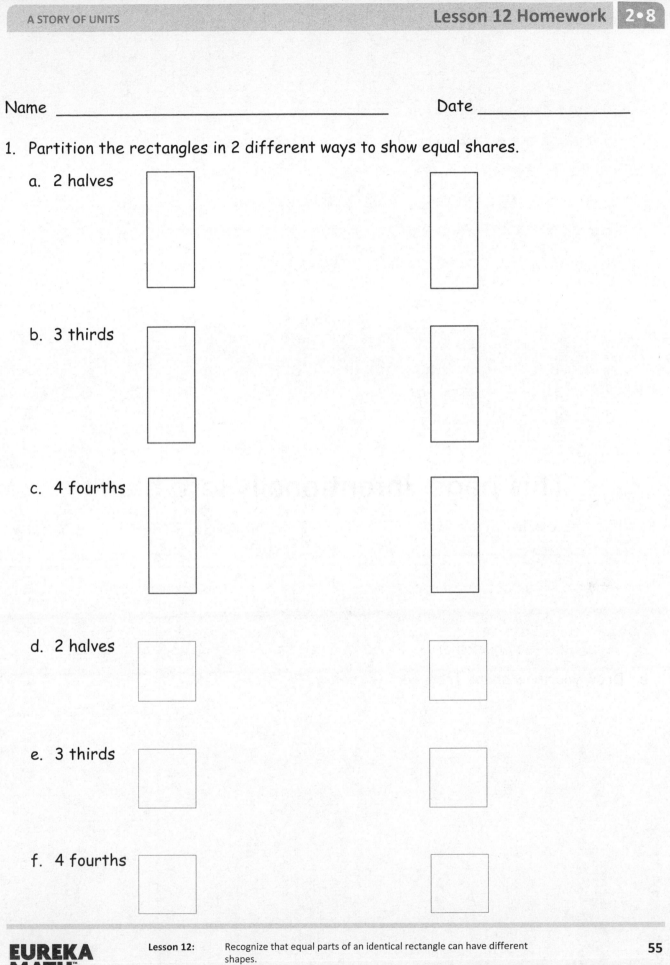

a. 2 halves

b. 3 thirds

c. 4 fourths

d. 2 halves

e. 3 thirds

f. 4 fourths

EUREKA MATH

Lesson 12:   Recognize that equal parts of an identical rectangle can have different shapes.

55

©2015 Great Minds. eureka-math.org
G2-M7M8-SE-B4-1.3.1-01.2016

This page intentionally left blank

2. Cut out the square at the bottom of this page.

   a. Cut the square in half to make 2 equal-size rectangles. Shade 1 half using your pencil.

   b. Rearrange the halves to create a new rectangle with no gaps or overlaps.

   c. Cut each equal part in half to make 4 equal-size squares.

   d. Rearrange the new equal shares to create different polygons.

   e. Draw one of your new polygons from Part (d) below. One half is shaded!

Lesson 12: Recognize that equal parts of an identical rectangle can have different shapes.

57

This page intentionally left blank

Name _____ Date _____

1. Tell what fraction of each clock is shaded in the space below using the words *quarter, quarters, half,* or *halves.*

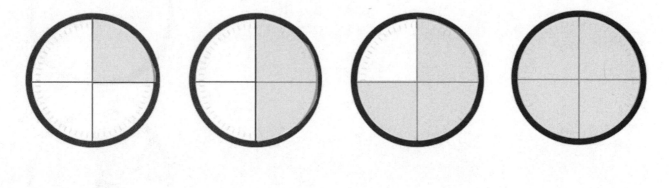

_____   _____   _____   _____

2. Write the time shown on each clock.

a.

_____

b.

_____

c.

_____

d.

_____

Lesson 13:   Construct a paper clock by partitioning a circle into halves and quarters, and tell time to the half hour or quarter hour.

59

©2015 Great Minds. eureka-math.org
G2-M7M8-SE-B4-1.3.1-01.2016

3. Match each time to the correct clock by drawing a line.

- Quarter to 4

- Half past 8

- 8:30

- 3:45

- 1:15

3. Draw the minute hand on the clock to show the correct time.

3:45   11:30   6:15

Lesson 13:   Construct a paper clock by partitioning a circle into halves and quarters, and tell time to the half hour or quarter hour.

EUREKA MATH

Name _____   Date _____

1. Tell what fraction of each clock is shaded in the space below using the words *quarter, quarters, half,* or *halves.*

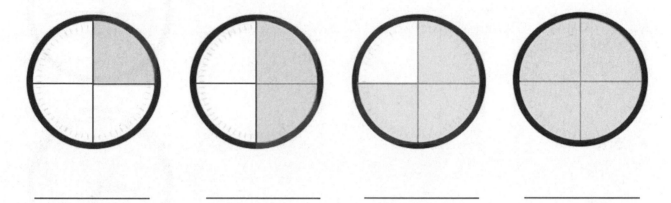

_____   _____   _____   _____

2. Write the time shown on each clock.

a.

_____

b.

_____

c.

_____

d.

_____

Lesson 13:   Construct a paper clock by partitioning a circle into halves and quarters, and tell time to the half hour or quarter hour.

61

3. Match each time to the correct clock by drawing a line.

- Quarter to 5

- Half past 5

- 5:15

- Quarter after 5

- 4:45

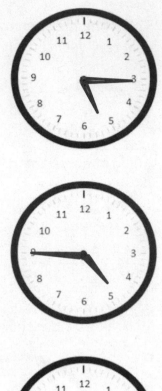

4. Draw the minute hand on the clock to show the correct time.

3:30   11:45   6:15

Lesson 13:   Construct a paper clock by partitioning a circle into halves and quarters, and tell time to the half hour or quarter hour.

Name _____   Date _____

1. Fill in the missing numbers.

    60, 55, 50, _____, 40, _____, _____, _____, 20, _____, _____, _____, _____

2. Fill in the missing numbers on the face of the clock to show the minutes.

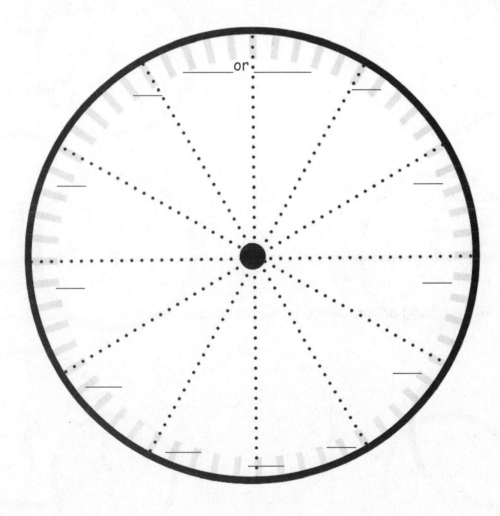

3. Draw the hour and minute hands on the clocks to match the correct time.

3:05   3:35

4:10   4:40

6:25   6:55

4. What time is it?

_____   _____

EUREKA
MATH

Name _____   Date _____

1. Fill in the missing numbers.

   0, 5, 10, _____, _____, _____, _____, 35, _____, _____, _____, _____, _____

   _____, _____, _____, 45, 40, _____, _____, _____, 20, 15, _____, _____, _____

2. Fill in the missing minutes on the face of the clock.

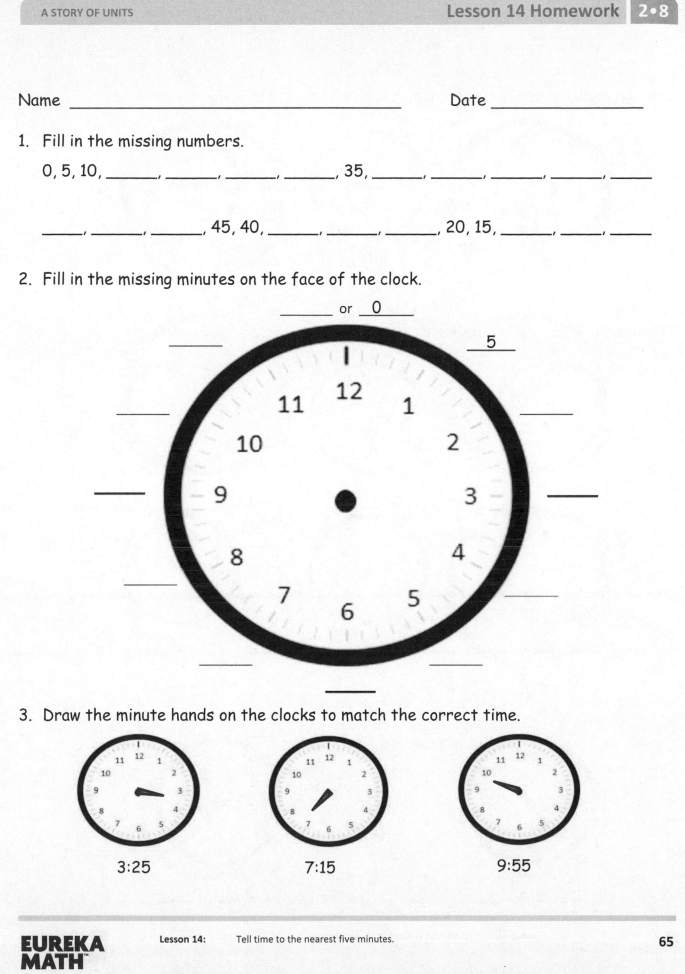

3. Draw the minute hands on the clocks to match the correct time.

   3:25   7:15   9:55

4. Draw the hour hands on the clocks to match the correct time.

12:30   10:10   3:45

5. Draw the hour and minute hands on the clocks to match the correct time.

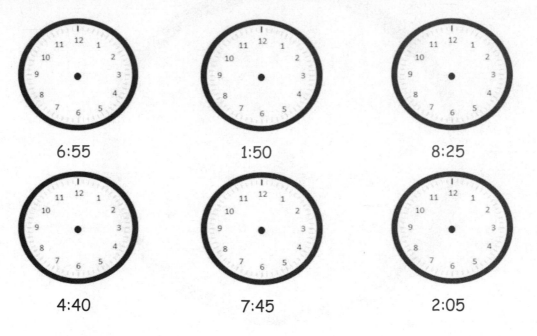

6:55   1:50   8:25

4:40   7:45   2:05

6. What time is it?

_____   _____

Lesson 14:   Tell time to the nearest five minutes.

©2015 Great Minds. eureka-math.org
G2-M7M8-SE-B4-1.3.1-01.2016

EUREKA
MATH™

Name _____   Date _____

1. Decide whether the activity below would happen in the a.m. or the p.m. Circle your answer.

   a. Waking up for school   **a.m. / p.m.**

   b. Eating dinner   **a.m. / p.m.**

   c. Reading a bedtime story   **a.m. / p.m.**

   d. Making breakfast   **a.m. / p.m.**

   e. Having a play date after school   **a.m. / p.m.**

   f. Going to bed   **a.m. / p.m.**

   g. Eating a piece of cake   **a.m. / p.m.**

   h. Eating lunch   **a.m. / p.m.**

EUREKA MATH

Lesson 15:   Tell time to the nearest five minutes; relate *a.m.* and *p.m.* to time of day.

67

©2015 Great Minds. eureka-math.org
G2-M7M8-SE-B4-1.3.1-01.2016

2. Draw the hands on the analog clock to match the time on the digital clock. Then, circle **a.m. or p.m.** based on the description given.

  a. Brushing your teeth after you wake up

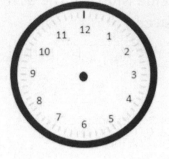

       7:10   **a.m. or p.m.**

  b. Finishing homework

       5:55   **a.m. or p.m.**

3. Write what you might be doing if it were **a.m. or p.m.**

  a. **a.m.** _____

  b. **p.m.** _____

4. What time does the clock show?

       _____ : _____

Lesson 15:   Tell time to the nearest five minutes; relate *a.m.* and *p.m.* to time of day.

Name _____ Date _____

1. Decide whether the activity below would happen in the a.m. or the p.m. Circle your answer.

a. Eating breakfast	a.m. / p.m.	b. Doing homework	a.m. / p.m.
c. Setting the table for dinner	a.m. / p.m.	d. Waking up in the morning	a.m. / p.m.
e. After-school dance class	a.m. / p.m.	f. Eating lunch	a.m. / p.m.
g. Going to bed	a.m. / p.m.	h. Heating up dinner	a.m. / p.m.

2. Write the time displayed on the clock. Then, choose whether the activity below would happen in the a.m. or the p.m.

a. Brushing your teeth before school	b. Eating dessert after dinner
____:____ a.m. / p.m.	____:____ a.m. / p.m.

EUREKA MATH

Lesson 15: Tell time to the nearest five minutes; relate *a.m.* and *p.m.* to time of day.

69

©2015 Great Minds. eureka-math.org
G2-M7M8-SE-B4-1.3.1-01.2016

3. Draw the hands on the analog clock to match the time on the digital clock. Then, circle **a.m.** or **p.m.** based on the description given.

   a. Brushing your teeth before bedtime

   | 8:15 | **a.m. or p.m.**

   b. Recess after lunch

   | 12:30 | **a.m. or p.m.**

4. Write what you might be doing if it were **a.m.** or **p.m.**

   a. **a.m.** _____

   b. **p.m.** _____

   c. **a.m.** _____

   d. **p.m.** _____

Lesson 15:   Tell time to the nearest five minutes; relate *a.m.* and *p.m.* to time of day.

EUREKA
MATH

Write the time. Circle a.m. or p.m.

a.m./p.m.

telling time story (large)

Lesson 15: Tell time to the nearest five minutes; relate *a.m.* and *p.m.* to time of day.

71

©2015 Great Minds. eureka-math.org
G2-M7M8-SE-B4-1.3.1-01.2016

Write the time.   Circle a.m. or p.m.

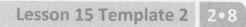

_____

a.m./p.m.

telling time story (large)

Lesson 15:   Tell time to the nearest five minutes; relate *a.m.* and *p.m.* to time of day.

Write the time. Circle a.m. or p.m.

a.m./p.m.

telling time story (large)

Write the time.   Circle a.m. or p.m.

a.m./p.m.

telling time story (large)

Lesson 15:   Tell time to the nearest five minutes; relate *a.m.* and *p.m.* to time of day.

Write the time. Circle a.m. or p.m.

_____

a.m./p.m.

telling time story (large)

Lesson 15:   Tell time to the nearest five minutes; relate *a.m.* and *p.m.* to time of day.

75

Write the time. Circle a.m. or p.m.

_____
a.m./p.m.

telling time story (large)

Lesson 15:   Tell time to the nearest five minutes; relate *a.m.* and *p.m.* to time of day.

©2015 Great Minds. eureka-math.org
G2-M7M8-SE-B4-1.3.1-01.2016

Write the time.　Circle a.m. or p.m.

_____
a.m./p.m.

_____
telling time story (large)

Lesson 15:　Tell time to the nearest five minutes; relate *a.m.* and *p.m.* to time of day.

77

Write the time. Circle a.m. or p.m.

_____

a.m./p.m.

telling time story (large)

Lesson 15:   Tell time to the nearest five minutes; relate *a.m.* and *p.m.* to time of day.

Name _____   Date _____

1. How much time has passed?

    a. 6:30 a.m. → 7:00 a.m.   _____

    b. 4:00 p.m. → 9:00 p.m.   _____

    c. 11:00 a.m. → 5:00 p.m.   _____

    d. 3:30 a.m. → 10:30 a.m.   _____

    e. 7:00 p.m. → 1:30 a.m.   _____

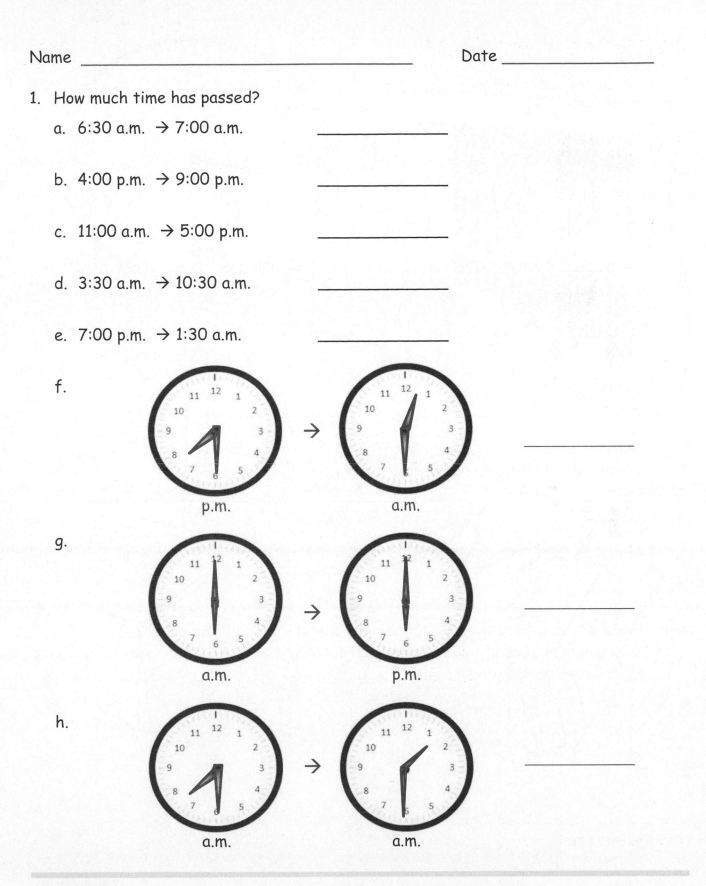

EUREKA
MATH™

Lesson 16:   Solve elapsed time problems involving whole hours and a half hour.

79

©2015 Great Minds. eureka-math.org
G2-M7M8-SE-B4-1.3.1-01.2016

2. Solve.

a. Tracy arrives at school at 7:30 a.m. She leaves school at 3:30 p.m. How long is Tracy at school?

b. Anna spent 3 hours at dance practice. She finished at 6:15 p.m. What time did she start?

c. Andy finished baseball practice at 4:30 p.m. His practice was 2 hours long. What time did his baseball practice start?

d. Marcus took a road trip. He left on Monday at 7:00 a.m. and drove until 4:00 p.m. On Tuesday, Marcus drove from 6:00 a.m. to 3:30 p.m. How long did he drive on Monday and Tuesday?

Lesson 16:   Solve elapsed time problems involving whole hours and a half hour.

Name _____   Date _____

1. How much time has passed?

a. 2:00 p.m. → 8:00 p.m.   _____

b. 7:30 a.m. → 12:00 p.m. (noon)   _____

c. 10:00 a.m. → 4:30 p.m.   _____

d. 1:30 p.m. → 8:30 p.m.   _____

e. 9:30 a.m. → 2:00 p.m.   _____

f.

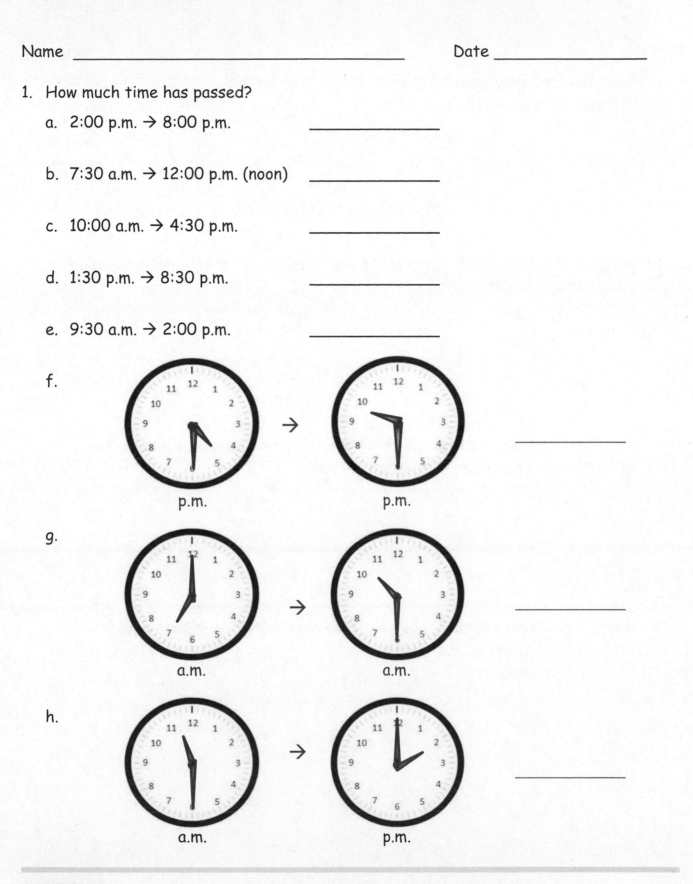

p.m.   p.m.   _____

g.

a.m.   a.m.   _____

h.

a.m.   p.m.   _____

EUREKA MATH

Lesson 16:   Solve elapsed time problems involving whole hours and a half hour.

81

©2015 Great Minds. eureka-math.org
G2-M7M8-SE-B4-1.3.1-01.2016

2. Solve.

   a. Kylie started basketball practice at 2:30 p.m. and finished at 6:00 p.m. How long was Kylie at basketball practice?

   b. Jamal spent 4 and a half hours at his family picnic. It started at 1:30 p.m. What time did Jamal leave?

   c. Christopher spent 2 hours doing his homework. He finished at 5:30 p.m. What time did he start his homework?

   d. Henry slept from 8 p.m. to 6:30 a.m. How many hours did Henry sleep?

Lesson 16:   Solve elapsed time problems involving whole hours and a half hour.

©2015 Great Minds. eureka-math.org
G2-M7M8-SE-B4-1.3.1-01.2016